IRISH FAMILY HISTORY ON

A DIRECTORY

Fourth Edition

STUART A. RAYMOND

The Family History Partnership

Published by
The Family History Partnership
57 Bury New Road
Ramsbottom, Bury
Lancashire BL0 0BZ

www.thefamilyhistorypartnership.com

First published 2001
Second edition 2004
Third edition 2007
Fourth edition 2015

ISBN: 978 1 906280 51 2

Copyright © Stuart A. Raymond

Printed in the United Kingdom
by Henry Ling Limited
at the Dorset Press
Dorchester DT1 1HD

Contents

Introduction

A vast amount of information concerning genealogy and family history is now available on the internet. Surfing the net can be a very productive process for the researcher; it can, however, also be very frustrating. There are thousands of genealogical web sites worth visiting, but the means for finding specific relevant sites are very poor. Search engines frequently list dozens of irrelevant sites, but not the ones required. 'Gateway' sites are not always easy to use. Links are not always kept up to date. It is easy for relevant sites to escape attention.

I hope that this directory will provide at least a partial means for overcoming these problems. It is intended to help you identify those sites most relevant to your research. The listing is, inevitably, selective. I have only included those sites likely to provide you with useful information. Sites devoted to specific sources, such as parish registers or monumental inscriptions, are only included where they include a substantial amount of information, and generally not where they only include 'selected' entries. I am suspicious of sites which do not indicate the sources of their information; these are mostly excluded. Sites devoted to particular families are excluded: a listing would occupy at least a whole volume. I have also excluded passenger list sites dealing with single voyages: again, a full listing would be extensive. For this edition, I have been forced to exclude individual mailing lists in order to save space. Most sites of general interest, e.g. search engines, maps, etc.,

are also excluded. Many of the sites I have listed, and especially those in chapters 1, 7 and 8, can be used to find sites excluded from this directory.

This listing is as up-to-date as I have been able to make it. However, new web pages are being mounted every day, and URLs change frequently. Consequently, it is anticipated that this directory will need frequent updating. If you are unable to find a site listed here, then use a search engine such as Google **www.google.com** to search words from the title – or perhaps the final portion of the URL. Alternatively, check Cyndis List or one of the other gateways listed in chapter 1. The probability is that the site has moved to another address. It is frequently the case that sites which have changed all or part of their URL can be found in this way.

If you know of sites which have not been listed here, or which are new, please let me know so that they may be included in the next edition of this directory. Many hundred websites are new to this edition; in particular, there are again much more extensive listings of sites relating to births, marriages and deaths, and to monumental inscriptions, so much so that the information given here has had to be greatly abbreviated.

My thanks go to Bob Boyd, who has again seen this edition through the press, and to my partners in the Family History Partnership.

1. Gateways, Search Engines etc.

There are a variety of gateways and search engines for Irish genealogists. One of the most useful is Genuki, which itself provides a great deal of general information. Cyndis list is the major international gateway; it has an American bias, but nevertheless provides numerous links to Irish sites. Quite a number of sites offer similar help, although the 'international' ones tend to be biased towards U.S. genealogy. General search engines are not listed here; they may be found on Cyndis List, or by accessing some of the other sites listed below.

- Genuki Ireland'
  www.genuki.org.uk/big/irl
- Cyndis List of Genealogy Sites on the Internet: Ireland & Northern Ireland
  www.cyndislist.com/ireland.htm
- Roots Web
  www.rootsweb.ancestry.com
  Home to thousands of genealogical mailing lists, the Genweb project, web sites, etc. American bias, but also of Irish interest.
- Ireland Genealogical Projects
  irelandgenealogyprojects.rootsweb.ancestry.com
  Lists county pages, query pages, etc.

- The Ireland Gen Web Project
  www.irelandgenweb.com

There are a variety of other gateway sites:
- All English Records.com: Ireland Genealogy Records
  www.allenglishrecords.com/ireland

- The Celtic Connection
  http://lorettawallace.net/ire.html
- Genealogy Ireland ~Eire ~History
  www.members.tripod.com/~Caryl_Williams/Eire-7.html
- Genealogy Resources on the Internet: Irish Genealogy
  www.genealogy.com/30_links.html
- Ireland Genealogy
  www.genealogy-of-uk.com/Ireland/index.html
- Ireland Genealogy Links
  www.genealogylinks.net/uk/Ireland
- Ireland: Web Sites for Genealogists
  www.coraweb.com.au/ireland.htm
- The Irish Archives
  www.theirisharchives.com
- Kindred Trails: Ireland (Irish) Genealogy & Family History Resources
  www.kindredtrails.com/ireland.html
- Irish Ancestral Pages
  www.geocities.ws/irishancestralpages/index-2.html
  Includes various databases.
- Irish Ancestry
  https://sites.google.com/site/freeirishancestry/home
  Links pages for each county.
- Irish Genealogy
  www.daddezio.com/irshgen.html
- Irish Genealogy Links
  www.genealogylinks.net/uk/ireland
- Irish Genealogy on the Net
  irishgenealogy.net
- John Grenham
  http://www.johngrenham.com/index.shtml#links/
  Includes useful links pages.

- Searcher: the Irish Genealogy Search Engine & Directory
  www.ireland-information.com/irishgenealogy
- Ireland Genealogy: UKI search.com
  www.ukisearch.com/ireland.html
- Mary's Genealogy Treasures: Ireland and Northern Ireland
  www.telusplanet.net/public/mtoll/ireland.htm

For a gateway to Irish genealogy in Canada, visit:
- Irish Genealogy in Canada
  www.layden-zella.tripod.com/IrishGen.index.html

If you want to place your research in the wider context of Irish history, see:
- John Stoners Sources for Irish History
  www.ocf.berkeley.edu/~stonerjw/eire_his.html

For a detailed bibliography of Irish history, visit:
- Irish History Online
  www.irishhistoryonline.ie

Sites which are no longer current may still be read at:
- Internet Archive Wayback Machine
  https://archive.org

2. General Introductions to Irish Genealogy

Numerous general guides to Irish genealogy are available on the internet; most provide similar basic guidance. Many family history society sites (chapter 4 below) have beginners' guides; so do many of the county pages listed in chapter 7. The websites of libraries and archives (see chapter 3) frequently provide excellent guidance. Some of the pages listed below are extensive - especially those from major institutions.

- Centre for Irish Genealogical and Historical Studies
  homepage.tinet.ie/~seanjmurphy
  Includes 'Directory of Irish genealogy', etc.
- Family Search: Ireland
  https://familysearch.org/learn/wiki/en/Ireland
  Sound advice, including county pages.
- Fianna Guide to Irish Genealogy
  www.rootsweb.com/~fianna
  Extensive, including county pages, and many databases
- Finding Your Ancestors in Ireland
  www.genealogy.com/genealogy/4_pocket.html?Welcome=1083401080
  For the descendants of emigrants; includes brief notes on sources in Australia, Canada, New Zealand, the U.S.A. and the U.K.
- From Ireland: Free Irish Genealogy
  www.from-ireland.net
  Extensive.
- Discovering Ireland: Genealogy
  www.discoveringireland.com/genealogy
- Ireland Roots
  http://irelandroots.com
  Introductory pages, including message boards for each county.

- Irish Ancestors
  www.irishtimes.com/ancestor/index.htm
  Useful advice pages; also county pages.
- Irish Ancestors.net
  http://freepages.genealogy.rootsweb.ancestry.com/~irishancestors/
- Irish Genealogy Toolkit
  www.irish-genealogy-toolkit.com/index.html
- Irish Research / Lyman D. Platt
  www.genealogy.com/4_irsrcs.html
  Brief introduction.
- Irish Research: Suggestions for the Beginner / Kyle Betit
  globalgenealogy.com/globalgazette/gazkb/gazkb33.htm
- When Your Irish Parish Registers Start Too Late / Kyle Betit
  globalgenealogy.com/globalgazette/gazkb/gazkb35.htm
- Your Irish Roots
  www.youririshroots.com
  Introductory pages.
- Seventeenth Century Sources
  http://freepages.genealogy.rootsweb.ancestry.com/~irishancestors/Add17.html
  Covers a wide range of sources, as do the following:
- Eighteenth Century Sources
  http://freepages.genealogy.rootsweb.ancestry.com/~irishancestors/Add18.html
- Nineteenth Century Sources
  http://freepages.genealogy.rootsweb.ancestry.com/~irishancestors/Add19.html
- Guide to Researching Irish Family/Social History in Dundee
  www.fdca.org.uk/Irish_History.html
- Irish Records Index, 1500-1920
  http://search.ancestry.co.uk/search/db.aspx?dbid=4077
  Index to a collection held by the Mormon's Family History Library.

For Northern Ireland, see:
- Northern Ireland Research: Selected Resources
  http://globalgenealogy.com/globalgazette/gazkb/gazkb60.htm

- Eddies Extracts
  http://freepages.genealogy.rootsweb.ancestry.com/~econnolly
  Extensive collection of extracts from Northern Ireland sources.
- Roulston, William. My roots: tracing your Belfast Ancestors. Ulster Historical Foundation, 2008.
  www.ancestryireland.com/wp-content/uploads/PDFs/my-roots.pdf

Overseas researchers may find the following helpful:
- Irish
  www.genealogy.com/00000374.html
  Brief.
- Irish Abroad
  www.irishabroad.com/YourRoots
- Irish and Irish-American Family Research
  mypage.siu.edu/edoday
  For American researchers.

Professional Help
If you want to employ a professional genealogist, you should first read:
- Employing a Professional Researcher: a practical guide
  www.sog.org.uk/learn/education-sub-page-for-testing-navigation/hints-tips-six-employing-a-professional-genealogist

Many professional genealogists have their own web page. These are not listed here, but many can be found using gateways such as Cyndi's List (see below). Professionals are listed by:
- Association of Professional Genealogists in Ireland
  www.apgi.ie
- Genealogy Researchers
  www.nationalarchives.ie/genealogy1/genealogy-researchers-nationwide
  Compiled by the National Archives of Ireland

- What's What in Irish Genealogy: Research Services
  http://indigo.ie/~gorry/Research.html
  Guidance on employing a professional, plus various lists of professional genealogists.

- Independent Commercial Researchers
  www.proni.gov.uk/index/research_and_records_held/can_someone_
      else_do_research_for_me/independent_commercial_researchers.htm
  At the Public Record Office of Northern Ireland.

3. Libraries, Record Offices and Books

Most of the information sought by genealogists is likely to be found in books and archival sources. The libraries and record offices which hold these resources provide an essential genealogical service, which is unlikely to be replaced by the internet. The value of the latter is in pointing you in the right direction, and helping you to identify the books and records you need to check. Many libraries and record offices now have webpages, listed here. Those which provide internet access to their catalogues are providing a particularly valuable service.

It is impossible here to provide a complete list of library and record office websites likely to be of use to genealogists. Such a list would have to include most public and university libraries, and is outside the scope of this book. However, a number of sites provide extensive listings. The Irish Times Irish Ancestors site includes listings of major repositories, and of local libraries in Eire and in Northern Ireland:

- Irish Ancestors
  www.irishtimes.com/ancestor/browse/#addresses
  Click 'contact addresses'

See also the National Archives of Ireland listing of:
- Genealogy Centres Nationwide
  www.nationalarchives.ie/genealogy1/genealogy-centres-nationwide/

A database of public libraries can be found at:
- Ask About Ireland
  www.askaboutireland.ie/

A general gateway to library sites is provided by:
- Libdex: Ireland
  www.libdex.com/country/Ireland.html
  For Northern Ireland, see **/Northern_Ireland.html.**

Libraries and record offices of particular interest to genealogists are listed in:
- Ireland Archives and Libraries
  https://familysearch.org/learn/wiki/en/Ireland_Archives_and_Libraries

For a union catalogue of over 70 UK and Irish university libraries, consult:
- Copac
  www.copac.ac.uk

Record offices are listed by:
- Learn About Archives: Archive Services
  www.learnaboutarchives.ie/index.php/archive-services/archive-
  services-pdf

See also:
- National Archives Discovery Catalogue
  www.discovery.nationalarchives.gov.uk
  Primarily concerned with the UK, bus also includes details of
  repositories in Northern Ireland and the Republic of Ireland. Use the
  'Find an Archive' search box.
- What's What in Irish Genealogy: Record Repositories
  indigo.ie/~gorry/Reposit.html

A union catalogue of Irish archives is provided by:
- Irish Archives Resource
  www.iar.ie/index.shtml

See also:
- RASCAL: Research & Special Collections Available Locally
  www.rascal.ac.uk

Major Institutions in Ireland
- National Archives of Ireland
  www.nationalarchives.ie
  Includes catalogue, a variety of research guides, & a number of
  databases (mostly listed below).
- A Guide to the National Archives of Ireland
  homepage.eircom.net/~seanjmurphy/nai
- National Library of Ireland
  www.nli.ie
  Includes catalogue, pages on 'family history research' in the National
  Library, details of collections, etc. For sources held, see also
  http://sources.nli.ie
- The Public Record Office of Northern Ireland
  www.proni.gov.uk
  Includes details of the extensive records held.
- Representative Church Body Library
  www.ireland.anglican.org/library
  Repository of the archives of the Church of Ireland.
- Mellon Centre for Migration Studies
  www.qub.ac.uk/cms
  Details of its library and 'emigration database'.
- Cardinal Tomás Ó Fiaich Library & Archive
  www.ofiaich.ie

Major Institutions Overseas
- The British Library
  www.bl.uk
  General information and public catalogue; holds extensive Irish collections.
- Family History Library
  www.familysearch.org
  Library of the Latter Day Saints. For details of its world-wide branch libraries
  (including those in Ireland), scroll down and click on 'Find a Centre'.

University Libraries
- Boole Library, University College Cork
  http://booleweb.ucc.ie/index.php?pageID=1
- Trinity College Library, Dublin
  www.tcd.ie/library
- Maynooth University: National University of Ireland, Maynooth: Library
  www.maynoothuniversity.ie/campus-life/campus-facilities/library
- University of Ulster Library Services
  www.library.ulster.ac.uk

Local Libraries & Archives

Antrim
- Linen Hall Library, Belfast
  www.linenhall.com
  The leading centre for Irish and local studies in Northern Ireland. Includes catalogue.

Armagh *See also Louth*
- Southern Education and Library Board: Irish & Local Studies Library
  www.selb.org/library/irish.htm

Carlow
- Carlow Libraries: Local History
  www.carlowlibraries.ie/localhistory.html

Clare
- Clare County Library
  www.clarelibrary.ie
  Includes pages on 'Genealogy', 'History', 'Clare County Archives', etc.

Cork
- Cork County Library & Arts Service
  www.corkcoco.ie/co/web/Cork%20County%20Council/ Departments/Library%20&%20Arts%20Service
  Includes pages on 'reference & local studies', & on 'trace your ancestors'.

- Cork City and County Archives Catalogue
  www.corkcity.ie/services
  Click on title.
- Cork City Libraries: Cork Local Studies
  www.corkcitylibraries.ie/central/corklocalstudies

Donegal
- Donegal Libraries & Information
  www.donegallibrary.ie
  Click on 'Local/Family History'.
- Donegal County Council: Archives
  www.donegalcoco.ie/culture/archives

Dublin
- Dublin City Public Libraries and Archive
  www.dublincity.ie/main-menu-services-recreation-culture/dublin-city-public-libraries-and-archive
  Click 'Research My Family Tree'.
- Dun Laoghaire-Rathdown Libraries
  http://libraries.dlrcoco.ie/
  Click on 'local History'.
- Fingal County Libraries
  www.fingalcoco.ie/community-and-leisure/libraries
  Includes page on 'Local Studies Library and Archives'

Galway
- Galway Public Library
  www.galwaylibrary.ie
  Includes page on 'Galway local history', linking to page on local archives.

Kerry
- Kerry County Library Local History and Archives Department
  www.kerrylibrary.ie
  Click on 'Local History'.

Kildare
- Kildare Collections and Research Services: Kildare Local Studies Department
  http://kildare.ie/Library/KildareCollectionsandResearchServices

Kilkenny
- Kilkenny County Library: Local Studies
  http://kilkennylibrary.kilkenny.ie/eng/Our_Services/Local_Studies/

Laois
- Laois County Council: Local Research
  http://www.laois.ie/LeisureandCulture/Libraries/LocalResearch

Leitrim
- Leitrim County Council: Local Studies
  www.leitrimcoco.ie/eng/Services_A-Z/Library//Local_Studies/

Limerick
- Limerick City & County Council: Local Studies
  www.limerickcity.ie/Library/LocalStudies
- Limerick Archives
  www.limerick.ie/Archives

Londonderry
- Derry City Council Heritage & Museum Service: Archive & Genealogy Service
  www.derrycity.gov.uk/Museums/Archive-Service

Longford
- Longford County Library
  www.longfordlibrary.ie
  Includes pages on archives & local studies.

Louth
- Louth County Archives Service
  www.louthcoco.ie/en/Services/Archives
- Cross Border Archives Project
  www.louthnewryarchives.ie/

Mayo
- Mayo County Library Local Studies
  www.mayolibrary.ie/en/LocalStudies

Meath
- Meath County Council Library Service
  www.meath.ie/Community/Libraries/
  Includes pages on 'local studies' & 'genealogy'.
- Archives and Libraries for Genealogical and Local Historical Research concerning County Meath
  www.angelfire.com/ak2/ashbourne/archives.html

Monaghan
- Monaghan County Library: Services
  www.monaghan.ie/en/services/library
  Includes page on 'Local History & Genealogy', including booklet on How to trace your ancestors in County Monaghan.

Offaly
- Offaly County Library: Local Studies and Archive Service
  www.offaly.ie/eng/Services/Libraries/Local_Studies_And_Archive_ Service

Roscommon
- Roscommon County Council: Local Studies and Archives
  www.roscommoncoco.ie/en/Services/Library/Local_Studies_and_ Archives

Sligo

- Sligo County Library: Local Studies
  www.sligolibrary.ie/sligolibrarynew/LocalStudies

Waterford

- Waterford City & County Libraries: Local Studies
  www.waterfordcity.ie/library/iguana/
  www.main.cls?surl=Local%20Studies
- Waterford City Archives
  www.waterfordcity.ie/departments/archives

Westmeath

- Westmeath County Council: Local Studies
  www.westmeathcoco.ie/en/ourservices/tourismartsrecreation/
  libraryservice/localstudies/

Wexford

- Wexford County Council: Local Studies Service
  www.wexford.ie/wex/Departments/Library/YourServices/
  LocalStudies

Wicklow

- Wicklow County Council Library Services
  www.wicklow.ie/library-services
  Includes pages on archives, family history, and local history

Irish Family History Foundation

This Foundation coordinates a network of government sponsored genealogical research centres which have computerised millions of records, especially the civil registers. The coordinating body is:
- Irish Family History Foundation
  www.irish-roots.net

For a listing of the centres, see:
- County Based Genealogical Centres Nationwide
  www.nationalarchives.ie/genealogy1/genealogy-centres-nationwide

Guidance in the use of these centres is provided by:
- Irish Heritage Centres
  https://familysearch.org/learn/wiki/en/Irish_Heritage_Centres

Antrim

- Ulster Historical Foundation
  www.ancestryireland.com
  Covers Co. Antrim and Co. Down.

Armagh

- Armagh Ancestry
  http://armagh.rootsireland.ie

Cavan

- Cavan Genealogy
  http://cavan.rootsireland.ie

Clare

- Clare Heritage and Genealogical Centre
  www.clareroots.com

Cork

- Mallow Heritage Centre
  http://corknortheast.rootsireland.ie/
  Covers north-eastern Co. Cork

Donegal

- Donegal Ancestry
  www.donegalancestry.com

Down

- Ulster Historical Foundation<: Co Down
  http://down.rootsireland.ie

Dublin

- Swords Heritage Centre
  http://dublinnorth.rootsireland.ie
  Covers North Dublin
- Dun Laoghaire Heritage Centre
  http://dublinsouth.rootsireland.ie/

Fermanagh

- Irish World Family History Services
  http://fermanagh.rootsireland.ie
  Covers Co. Fermanagh and Co. Tyrone.

Galway

- East Galway Family History Society
  http://galwayeast.rootsireland.ie
- Galway Family History West
  http://galwaywest.rootsireland.ie/

Kildare

- Kildare Genealogy
  http://kildare.rootsireland.ie

Kilkenny

- Kilkenny Archaeological Society
  www.kilkennyarchaeologicalsociety.ie

Laois

- Irish Midlands Ancestry
  http://laois.rootsireland.ie

Leitrim

- Leitrim Genealogy Centre
  www.leitrimroots.com

Limerick

- Limerick Genealogy
  www.limerickgenealogy.com

Londonderry

- Derry Genealogy
  www.irish-roots.net/derry.asp

Longford

- Longford Genealogy
  http://longford.rootsireland.ie

Louth

- Louth Co. Library
  http://louth.rootsireland.ie/

Mayo

- Mayo Family History Centres
  http://mayo.rootsireland.ie

Meath

- Meath Heritage Centre
  www.meathroots.com

Offaly

- Offaly Historical & Archaeological Society
  www.offalyhistory.com

Roscommon

- County Roscommon Heritage and Genealogy Company
  www.roscommonroots.com

Sligo
- County Sligo Heritage and Genealogy Centre
  www.sligoroots.com

Tipperary
- Tipperary Family History Research
  www.tfhr.org

- Brú Ború Heritage Centre
  http://tipperarysouth.rootsireland.ie
  Covers South Tipperary.
- North Tipperary Genealogy Centre
  http://tipperarynorth.rootsireland.ie/

Tyrone *See Fermanagh*

Waterford
- Genealogy Waterford Ireland
  www.iol.ie/~mnoc/

Westmeath
- Dún na Si Heritage Centre
  www.iol.ie/~mnoc
  Covers Co. Westmeath

Wexford
- Wexford Genealogy
  http://wexford.rootsireland.ie/

Wicklow
- Wicklow Family History Centre
  http://wicklow.rootsireland.ie

Books
It is vital that the genealogist should be aware of the thousands of published books that may be of assistance in research. They contain far more information than is available on the web. A number of websites specialise in digitising books which are out of copyright. Many of these books are likely to be relevant to your reseach. Amongst others, these websites include:
- Family History Books
  https://books.familysearch.org/primo_library/libweb/action/search.do
- Internet Archive
  https://archive.org
- Google Books
  http://books.google.co.uk
- Open Library
  https://openlibrary.org

Bibliographies will help you to identify the specific books that you need. A number are available on the web, and are listed here. Once you have identified the book(s) you need, you may find them on one of the websites just mentioned; otherwise, check the catalogues of the libraries listed above (or your local library). Web-based bibliographies include:
- Genealogical Publications
  www.nationalarchives.ie/genealogy1/genealogical-publications
- Sources: A National Library of Ireland database for Irish research, contains over 180,000 catalogue records for Irish manuscripts, and for articles in Irish periodicals
  http://sources.nli.ie/About/Contents
- Allen County Public Library Genealogy Centre: Irish Guide
  www.genealogycenter.org/Pathfinders/Guides/Irish.aspx
  Bibliographic guide from an American library.
- Irish Genealogy
  www.newberry.org/irish-genealogy
  Bibliography from the Newberry Library, Chicago.

- Sources for Research in Irish Genealogy
  www.loc.gov/rr/genealogy/bib_guid/ireland.html
  Library of Congress bibliography.
- Local and Parish Histories of Ireland
  www.irishgenealogy.com/ireland/parish-histories.htm
- Northern Irish References: Ulster Province Family History
  www.rootsweb.com/~fianna/NIR/
  Bibliographic guide, with pages on Co's Antrim, Armagh, Donegal,
  Down, Fermanagh, Londonderry, Monaghan, and Tyrone.

For books on the Irish overseas, see:
- The Irish in ...
  www.bl.uk/reshelp/findhelpsubject/history/irishdiaspora/theirishin/
  theirishin.html
  On 'The Irish and Empire', see also **/theirishandempire/ireempire.html**

Antrim
- Books About Co. Antrim
  www.from-ireland.net/books-about-county-antrim

Armagh
- Books About Co. Armagh
  www.from-ireland.net/books-about-county-armagh

Cavan
- Books About Co. Cavan
  www.from-ireland.net/books-about-county-cavan

Clare
- Books about Co. Clare
  www.from-ireland.net/books-about-county-clare

Donegal
- County Donegal Books and Authors
  http://freepages.genealogy.rootsweb.ancestry.com/~donegal/books.htm

Fermanagh
- Books about Co. Fermanagh
  www.from-ireland.net/books-about-county-fermanagh

Kildare
- Kavanagh's Historical Bibliography of County Kildare
  http://kildare.ie/library/Bibliography/index.asp

Longford
- A Bibliography of County Longford based on the collection of books and
  journals in the Local Studies Department of Longford County Library
  www.longfordlibrary.ie/lib_inside.aspx?id=21580
- County Longford: a Bibliography
  www.igp-web.com/Longford/longbib.htm

Louth
- County Louth Ireland Genealogical Sources: Further Reading
  www.jbhall.freeservers.com/oldIndex.html

Sligo
- County Sligo, Ireland: Books
  www.rootsweb.ancestry.com/~irlsli/books.html
  Lists books with purchasing details

Tipperary
- Tipperary Books: a Bibliography
  www.igp-web.com/tipperary/tipbib.htm

Tyrone
- Research Resources: Books, Magazines & Microfilm Lists
  www.cotyroneireland.com/research.html

4. Family History Societies

Many Irish family history societies have websites. These generally provide information on the society - names of officers, meetings, membership information, publications, services offered, lists of members' interests, links to other web pages, *etc.* For an introduction to their work, see:
- Irish family tree research societies and local history groups
  www.irish-genealogy-toolkit.com/Irish-family-tree-research.html

A number of listings of societies are available:
- Family History and Genealogy Societies: Ireland
  www.genuki.org.uk/Societies/Ireland.html
- Federation of Family History Societies: Irish Societies
  www.ffhs.org.uk/members2/ireland.php
- Ireland Societies
  https://familysearch.org/learn/wiki/en/Ireland_Societies
- Irish Genealogical Societies and Periodicals/Kyle Betit
  globalgenealogy.com/globalgazette/gazkb/gazkb45.htm

For local history societies, see:
- Federation of Local History Societies
  www.localhistory.ie

National & Regional Organisations
- Council of Irish Genealogical Organisations
  indigo.ie/~gorry/CIGO.html
- Genealogical Society of Ireland
  www.familyhistory.ie
- Irish Family History Society
  www.ifhs.ie
- North of Ireland Family History Society
  www.nifhs.org

- Irish Palatine Association
  www.irishpalatines.org
  For German migrants to Ireland.

County & Local Societies

Armagh
- North Armagh Family History Society
  www.nafhs.org

Cork
- Cork Genealogical Society
  www.corkgenealogicalsociety.com
- Mallow Archaeological & Historical Society
  www.rootsweb.ancestry.com/~irlmahs
  For northern Co. Cork.

Offaly
- Offaly Historical & Archaeological Society
  www.offalyhistory.com

Overseas Societies

Australia
- Australian Institute of Genealogical Studies Inc. Ireland Interest Group
  www.aigs.org.au/irelandIG.htm
- Genealogical Society of Victoria: Irish Ancestry Group
  www.gsv.org.au/activities/groups/iag
- Western Australian Genealogical Society Inc. Irish Group
  http://membership.wags.org.au/special-interest-groups-mainmenu-47/irish-sig

England
- Irish Genealogical Research Society
  www.irishancestors.ie

- Manchester & Lancashire Family History Society: Irish Ancestry Branch
  www.mlfhs.org.uk/IAG

New Zealand
- New Zealand Society of Genealogists: Irish Interest Group
  www.genealogy.org.nz/Irish_Interest_Group_202.aspx

United States
- Irish Genealogical Society International
  www.irishgenealogical.org
  Based in Minneapolis area, Minnesota.
- American Irish Historical Society
  www.aihs.org
- Buffalo Irish Genealogical Society
  http://bigs.limewebs.com
- British Isles Family History Society-U.S.A: Irish Study Group
  www.rootsweb.ancestry.com/~bifhsusa/study-irish.html
- Irish American Archives Society
  www.irisharchives.org
  Irish emigrants to Cleveland, Ohio
- The Irish Ancestral Research Association
  www.tiara.ie
  Based in Massachusetts
- Irish Family History Forum
  www.ifhf.org
  Based in New York.
- Irish Genealogical Society of Michigan
  http://miigsm.org
- Irish Genealogical Society of Wisconsin
  www.igswonline.com

5. Discussion Groups: Mailing Lists, Newsgroups, & Message Boards

Want to ask someone who knows? Then join a discussion group. There are two main types. Message boards enable you to post queries online, and to receive replies. These are frequently gatewayed to mailing lists, on which communication is via email. There are many hundred Irish groups, too many to list here. They cover a wide range of subjects – surnames, specific places, specialist topics ranging from adoptees to the medieval period. Several detailed listings are available; the most comprehensive is:
- Genealogy Resources on the Internet: Ireland mailing lists
  www.rootsweb.com/~jfuller/gen_mail_country-unk-irl.html

See also:
- Genealogy Discussion Groups
  www.genuki.org.uk/indexes/MailingLists.html
- Cyndi's List: Mailing Lists
  http://www.cyndislist.com/mailing-lists
  Also click on 'Queries & Message Boards' & 'Newsgroups'

Many mailing lists are provided by Rootsweb. See:
- Mailing Lists
  http://lists.rootsweb.ancestry.com/index/index.html
  This includes a separate page listing Irish lists, but there are a variety of other lists which may also yield information.

For Rootsweb message boards, see:
- Message Boards: Ireland
  http://boards.rootsweb.com/localities.britisles.ireland/mb.ashx
  List

Many discussion groups are also available on:
- Google Groups
  https://groups.google.com/forum/#!overview
- Yahoo Groups
  https://groups.yahoo.com/neo/dir
- The British Isles Gen Web Project: Ireland Related Mailing Lists
  www.britishislesgenweb.org/irelandmail.htm

A number of sites offer message boards for every Irish county. These include:
- Cousin Connect
  www.cousinconnect.com
- Genforum: Ireland: Regions
  genforum.genealogy.com/ireland/regions.html

6. County & Local Pages

A great deal of information is to be found on county and local pages. A number of private individuals have created their own county pages, but a number of organisations and individuals have provided pages for every Irish county. There are too many of these to list each individual county page. Links can be found on the main pages of each of the following sites:

- Fianna
  www.rootsweb.ancestry.com/~fianna/
  Wide range of general information on resources, with various lists of sources, and many links.
- From Ireland
  www.from-ireland.net
  Include information under standard headings such as 'gravestones', ' journals', 'religious records', 'links', *etc.*
- Genuki
  www.genuki.org.uk/big/irl
  Primarily concerned with historical information, rather than on-going and completed research. Includes separate pages for each parish.
- The Ireland Genweb Project
  www.irelandgenweb.com
  Also has some similar information but also includes query boards for each county, and has more information on current and completed research; also query boards for each county.
- Ireland Genealogical Projects
  www.igp-web.com
  Has many transcripts and indexes of original sources.

- Irish Ancestors
  www.irishtimes.com/ancestor
  Includes standardised lists of sources for each county, e.g. census, directories, estate records, graveyards (i.e.monumental inscriptions), *etc*. Also maps of civil and Roman Catholic parishes, with lists of resources for each Roman Catholic parish. Many links.
- Irish Archives: Counties
  www.theirisharchives.com/counties
  Links pages.
- [Irish Genealogy]
  www.irishgenealogy.com
  Scroll down to 'counties in Ireland'.
- John Grenham
  www.johngrenham.com/
  This author has provided useful links pages for every county. Click 'genealogy links'.

For a listing of county websites on Rootsweb, see:
- Ireland and Northern Ireland
  www.rootsweb.com/~websites/international/uk.html#ireland
  In addition to the major web-sites, there are a number of stand-alone county and local pages, which are listed below. Note, however, that there are far too many parish websites to list them all.

Antrim
- Ballymoney Ancestry
  www.ballymoneyancestry.com
  Includes genealogical database based on many sources.
- Bann Valley Genealogy
  www.torrens.org.uk/Genealogy/BannValley
  Border of Co. Antrim & Co. Londonderry.

Armagh
- Lurgan Ancestry
  www.lurganancestry.com/index.html
  Includes many transcripts of sources.

Cavan
- Co. Cavan, Ireland, Research Site
  http://freepages.genealogy.rootsweb.ancestry.com/~adrian/Cavan.htm
- Bawnboy & Templeport Local Genealogical & Historical Data
  www.bawnboy.com/local-genealogy
  Includes many local sources.

Clare
- County Clare, Ireland
  www.connorsgenealogy.com/clare

Cork
- Cork
  http://freepages.genealogy.rootsweb.ancestry.com/~nyirish/CORK%20index
  Includes extracts from various sources.
- County Cork
  http://freepages.genealogy.rootsweb.ancestry.com/~mturner/cork/ire.cork.htm
  Many brief extracts from sources.
- Ginni Swanton's Web Site: County Cork Genealogy Information and Records
  http://www.ginnisw.com/corkmain.html
  Includes transcripts and indexes etc. of many sources for Co. Cork.
- Bandon Genealogy: a guide to tracing your ancestors in Bandon, Cork. Ireland
  www.bandon-genealogy.com

Derry *See* Londonderry

Donegal
- Donegal, Ireland
  **http://freepages.genealogy.rootsweb.ancestry.com/~donegaleire/
  Doncontent.html**
- Donegal Genealogy Resources
  http://freepages.genealogy.rootsweb.ancestry.com/~donegal
  Includes many parish pages.
- S.W. Donegal Irish Genealogy & our Irish Heritage
  **www.lineages.co.uk/2004/09/08/sw-donegal-irish-genealogy-our-
  irish-heritage/**

Down
- Raymonds County Down Website
  www.raymondscountydownwebsite.com
  Includes some parish pages.
- Ros Davies' Co. Down, Northern Ireland, Family History Research Site
  http://freepages.genealogy.rootsweb.ancestry.com/~rosdavies/index.html
- Newry, Donaghmore, Loughbrickland & Banbridge Genealogy Site
  http://freepages.genealogy.rootsweb.ancestry.com/~donaghmore1/

Fermanagh
- Fermanagh GOLD Members Genealogy Pages
  www.fermanagh-gold.com
  Miscellaneous submitted data.

Kerry
- County Kerry Genealogy
  www.rootsweb.com/~irlker/find.html

Leitrim
- Leitrim-Roscommon Genealogy Web Site
  www.leitrim-roscommon.com

Limerick
- Researcher's Handbook
  www.limerickcity.ie/Library/LocalStudies/ResearchersHandbook
  Covering Co. Limerick.
- County Limerick, Ireland
  www.connorsgenealogy.com/LIM/index.htm
- County Limerick Genealogy
  www.countylimerickgenealogy.com

Londonderry *See* Antrim

Louth
- County Louth, Ireland, Genealogical Sources
  www.jbhall.freeservers.com
  Includes many name lists

Mayo
- Irish Roots: My Irish Eyes from Co. Mayo Ireland
  http://freepages.genealogy.rootsweb.ancestry.com/~deesegenes
  Many extracts from sources.
- Family History in North County Mayo
  www.goldenlangan.com

Roscommon *See* Leitrim

Tipperary
- County Tipperary, Ireland
  www.connorsgenealogy.com/tipp
- Genealogical Research: Clogheen & District
  www.iol.ie/~clogheen/clogheen/clogpage/roots.html

Tyrone
- The County of Tyrone Ireland Genealogical Research Website
  www.cotyroneireland.com
- Bready Ancestry
  www.breadyancestry.com/index.php?id=3
  Includes various databases for Bready, Donagheady & Leckpatrick.

Wexford
- [Wexford]
  **http://freepages.genealogy.rootsweb.ancestry.com/~nyirish/
                              WEXFORD%20%20Index.html**
  Includes extracts from various sources
- Wexford Genealogy
  www.from-ireland.net/county-wexford-genealogy
  From Ireland

7. Surnames

The Internet is an invaluable aid for those who want to make contact with others researching the same surname. There are innumerable lists of surname interests, family web-sites, and surname mailing lists. The two latter categories will not be listed here; they are far too numerous for a book of this length, and many are international in scope rather than purely Irish. Such sites may be found through the surname web pages listed below.

For general guidance on researching Irish names, see:
- Researching Irish Names
  www.rootsweb.ancestry.com/~fianna/surname
  Includes many pages, including a gateway to Irish surname websites.

On the origin, history, and meanings of Irish names, see
- The Origin of Irish Family Names
  www.ireland-information.com/heraldichall/irishsurnames.htm
- Category: Surnames of Irish origin
  http://en.wikipedia.org/wiki/Category:Surnames_of_Irish_origin
- Surnames in Ireland
  http://freepages.genealogy.rootsweb.ancestry.com/~irishsurnames
- Ireland Names Personal
  https://familysearch.org/learn/wiki/en/Ireland_Military_Records
- Norman and Cambro-Norman Surnames of Ireland
  www.rootsweb.ancestry.com/~irlkik/ihm/irename2.htm
- Old Irish-Gaelic Surnames
  www.rootsweb.ancestry.com/~irlkik/ihm/irenames.htm
- Origin & Meaning of Irish Surnames
  **www.dochara.com/the-irish/surnames/origin-meaning-of-irish-
                                                    surnames**
- Surnames Common in Ireland at end of 16th century
  **http://irelandgenealogyprojects.rootsweb.ancestry.com/Old_IGW/
                                                    names.html**
  Includes page for 17th c.

On first names, see:
- Irish First Names
  www.dochara.com/the-irish/first-names/irish-first-names
- Irish Names: traditional, modern, and in-between
  www.namenerds.com/irish/
  Meanings of first names.

For the distribution of surnames, see:
- An Atlas of Irish Names
  www.ucc.ie/research/atlas
- Atlas of Family Names in Ireland
  http://publish.ucc.ie/doi/atlas
- Irish Abroad: County Surnames
  www.irishabroad.com/yourroots/genealogy/names/county
- Using Distribution Studies to Identify the Place of Origin of Your Irish
  Ancestors
  www.ajmorris.com/roots/ireland/dist.htm
  This article is accompanied by maps showing the distribution of
  surnames at /dig/dst/index.htm.
- Distribution of Surnames/Householders Report, Ulster, mid-19th century
  www.ancestryireland.com/family-records/distribution-of-
  surnames-griffiths-valuation-and-tithe-applotment-survey-
  in-ulster-mid-19th-century
  Subscription required.
- Distribution of Surnames in Ireland in 1890
  www.ancestryireland.com/family-records/distribution-of-surnames-
  in-ireland-1890-mathesons-special-report/
  Subscription required. From the book by Sir Robert E. Matheson,
  which is based on information from the indexes of the General Register
  Office. Also available (pay per view) at several other websites:
  www.worldvitalrecords.com/indexinfo.aspx?ix=gpc0806301872_
  specialreportonsurnamesinireland
  www.ajmorris.com/dig/toc/_01irsu.htm
  search.ancestry.co.uk/search/db.aspx?htx=BookList&dbid=7257.

A variety of databases can be searched for surnames at:
- Surname Navigator Ireland
  www.geneaservice.nl/navigator/ireland

Surname variations are discussed by:
- Irish Surname Variations
  www.from-ireland.net/gravestone-records/surname-variations/

Surname Web Pages
Surname web pages are listed in the following pages:
- Websites for surnames starting with 'a'.
  www.johngrenham.com/links/surnames/surnames_a.shtml#links/
- Irish Surname - Genealogy
  www.jackreidy.com/genealogy/surnames.htm
- Top 50 Irish Surnames
  www.genealogyforum.rootsweb.com/gfaol/surnames/Irish.htm
- A Z of Ireland Family Surnames Pages
  http://members.tripod.com/caryl_williams/Eirenames-7.html
- Cyndis List: Personal Research
  www.cyndislist.com/personal
  Good starting point, but with American bias. See also **/surnames**.
- Irish Surnames and Irish Descendants Homepages
  www.oocities.org/heartland/meadows/4404/pages.html
  Brief gateway.
- Surname Resources at RootsWeb
  http://resources.rootsweb.ancestry.com/surnames/
  International, but with many Irish names. To search, visit
  http://rsl.rootsweb.ancestry.com.
- Surname Helper Home Page
  http://surhelp.rootsweb.ancestry.com
  Gateway.
- Registry of Websites at Rootsweb
  http://www.rootsweb.ancestry.com/~websites
  Scroll down to 'surname websites'; probably the most extensive listing of
  surname sites; American bias
- Websites for Irish Surnames
  www.irishtimes.com/ancestor/fuses/surnameurls/
  index.cfm?fuseaction=ShowListing&startletter=a#links/
- Surnames in Ireland
  www.Irish Surnames.net

Surname Interests

Surnames currently being researched are recorded on a number of surname interest websites, which enable you to make contact with others researching the same family as yourself. The major published directory (which has now ceased publication) has been digitised at:

- International Genealogical Research Directory 1981-1993
  www.findmypast.co.uk/articles/world-records/full-list-of-australia-and-new-zealand-records/newspapers-directories-and-social-history/international-genealogical-research-directory-1981-1993

Other national interest lists include:
- Curious Fox: Ireland
  www.curiousfox.com/uk/ireland.lasso
- Genuki Surname Lists
  www.genuki.org.uk/indexes/SurnamesLists.html
- Ireland GenWeb Project: Surname Registry
  www.irelandgenweb.com/surnames
  Click under the title.
- The Irish Ancestral Research Association: Members Surname Interests
  www.tiara.ie/surnames.htm
- Irish Abroad: Irish Family Name Register
  www.irishabroad.com/Genealogy/SurnameInfo/urnameinformation_search.asp
- UK Surnames
  http://uk-surnames.com
  Scroll down & click on any county for a separate surname listing.

Regional, County and Local Surname Websites

Both interest lists and gateways/links pages to websites are included in the following list.

Antrim
- Co. Antrim Families on the Web
  www.oocities.org/heartland/prairie/4592/antlink.html
  Outdated, but may still be useful.
- The Antrim County Surname List
  http://www.ole.net/~maggie/antrim/surnames.htm

- Co. Antrim Surname Interest List
  www.irishgenealogy.net/forum/phpbb3/viewforum.php?f=17

Carlow
- County Carlow Surname Registry
  www.rootsweb.ancestry.com/~irlcar2/registry.htm
- Carlow 'roll-call'
  www.rootsweb.ancestry.com/~irlcar2/Carlow_Roll_Call_ind.htm
  Surname interests.

Cavan
- Surnames of County Cavan Only Interest List
  https://sites.google.com/site/countycavanirelandgenweb/surname-interest-list

Clare
- County Clare Surname Roster
  www.connorsgenealogy.com/clare/claresurnamesAtoD.htmlInterest list

Cork
- Ginni Swanton's Web Site: County Cork Surnames Database
  www.ginnisw.com/Surnames%20Home.htm

Donegal
- County Donegal Surname Researchers
  http://freepages.genealogy.rootsweb.ancestry.com/~donegaleire/Donresearch.html
  Gateway to web pages.
- Donegal Surnames being Researched
  http://freepages.genealogy.rootsweb.ancestry.com/~donegal/donpass.htm

Down
- Co. Down Family Genealogies
  www.rootsweb.ancestry.com/~nirdow/genealogies.htm
- Message Board
  http://freepages.genealogy.rootsweb.ancestry.com/~rosdavies/WORDS/RollCall.htm
  Interests list for Co. Down.

- People's Names of Co. Down, Ireland
  **http://freepages.genealogy.rootsweb.ancestry.com/~rosdavies/
  SURNAMES/Afrontpage.htm**
  Database, 800,000 names.

Galway
- County Galway Surname List
  www.rootsweb.ancestry.com/~irlgalway/galway.htm
- County Galway GenWeb Project: Family History Home Pages
  www.rootsweb.ancestry.com/~irlgal/homepagesam.htm
- County Galway Surname Queries: Surname Interests Prior to 2005
  www.rootsweb.ancestry.com/~irlgal/surnames.htm
- County Galway: Surname Registry Page
  www.igp-web.com/Galway/surnames.htm

Kerry
- Family Association Websites
  www.rootsweb.ancestry.com/~irlker/familywebs.html
  For Co. Kerry

Kilkenny
- County Kilkenny Ireland: Genealogy and History: Query Index and
  Submission Page
  www.rootsweb.ancestry.com/~irlkik/kquery.htm
- Surnames of Co. Kilkenny
  www.rootsweb.ancestry.com/~irlkik/ksurname.htm
- County Kilkenny Surnames
  www.rootsweb.ancestry.com/~irlkik2
  Click 'Surnames' for a registry.

Laois
- County Laois/Leix/Queens: Laois Surname Registry
  **freepages.family.rootsweb.ancestry.com/~mjbrennan/laois_
  registry_index.htm**
- County Leix Surname Registry
  www.connorsgenealogy.com/Leix/surnames.htm

Leitrim
- County Leitrim Surname Registry
  www.connorsgenealogy.net/Leitrim/surnames.htm
- County Leitrim Surnames
  www.irelandgenweb.com/irllet/surnames.htm
  Links page to family sites.
- Leitrim Roscommon Surname Search Page
  www.leitrim roscommon.com/surname_intro.html

Limerick
- County Limerick Surname Roster
  www.connorsgenealogy.com/LIM/limericksurnamesAtoF.html
  Continued at **/limericksurnamesGtoL.html,
  limericksurnamesMtoR.html, & /limericksurnamesStoZ.html**
- County Limerick Surnames
  www.countylimerickgenealogy.com/limerick_surnames.php
  Links to surname websites.
- Family Histories
  www.limerickcity.ie/Library/LocalStudies/FamilyHistories/
  From Limerick.

Londonderry
- Derry Surname Registry
  www.igp-web.com/Derry/surnames_for_derry.htm
  Interests list
- Londonderry Surname Queries
  www.thauvin.net/chance/ireland/derry/queries.jsp

Longford
- Longford Surnames Online
  www.igp-web.com/Longford/longford.htm
  Links page

Mayo
- The County Mayo Surname Interest List
  http://genuki.cs.ncl.ac.uk/SurnamesList/MAY.html
- County Mayo Surnames
  www.irelandgenweb.com/irlmay/surnames.htm

Meath
- County Meath Surnames, Lineages, Family Histories
  www.rootsweb.ancestry.com/~irlmea2/Surname/lineages.htm
  Interests list

Roscommon *See also Leitrim*

- Roscommon Surnames: Surname Registry
  www.igp-web.com/Roscommon/registry.htm
- Roscommon Surnames
  www.rootsweb.ancestry.com/~irlros/surnames.htm
  General discussion of surnames, with lists of common ones

Sligo
- County Sligo, Ireland: Surname Registry Page
  www.igp-web.com/Sligo/surnamereg.htm

Tipperary
- Tipperary Surname Registry
  www.igp-web.com/tipperary/registry.htm
  Interests list.
- County Tipperary Surnames Roster
  www.connorsgenealogy.com/tipp/tipperarysurnamesAtoD.html
- County Tipperary Surnames
  www.irelandgenweb.com/irltip/surnames.htm
  Includes interest lists and gateway to family web pages.
- Tipperary Surnames
  homepages.ihug.co.nz/~hughw/tip.html
  Interests list.

Tyrone
- County Tyrone Surname Project
  www.rootsweb.ancestry.com/~nirtyr/co-tyrone-surname.htm
  Interests list.

- County Tyrone: Surnames
  www.cotyroneireland.com/menus/surnames.html
  Links to surname webpages.

Ulster
- Ulster Historical Foundation: Members' Research Interests
  www.ancestryireland.com/family-records/members-research-interests
- Distribution of Surnames/Householders Report, Ulster, mid-19th century
  www.ancestryireland.com/family-records/distribution-of-surnames-griffiths-valuation-and-tithe-applotment-survey-in-ulster-mid-19th-century/
  In Ulster.

Westmeath
- County Westmeath Surname Registry
  www.igp-web.com/westmeath/registry.htm

Wexford
- The Wexford Surnames List
  http://homepages.ihug.co.nz/~hughw/wexford.html

8. Births, Marriages And Deaths

This chapter lists websites dealing with civil registers, parish registers, monumental inscriptions, and newspaper announcements, in one sequence. I have excluded pages which only have selected entries, or which only cover a few years. A useful gateway to marriage records is provided by:

- County Ireland Marriage Records
  http://genealogylinks.net/marriages/uk/ireland/index.html

Introductions: Civil Registration
For indexes and databases, see below, p.27.
- Irish Civil Records
  www.from-ireland.net/irish-civil-records
  Includes a detailed explanation, together with county indexes not otherwise listed below.
- Civil Registration
  http://freepages.genealogy.rootsweb.ancestry.com/~irishancestors/Civil%20registration.html
- Finding Irish Civil Registration Records
  https://fortheloveofancestors.wordpress.com/2012/11/20/finding-irish-civil-registration-records
- Ginni Swanton's Web Site: Irish Birth, Death, and Marriage Civil Records
  www.ginnisw.com/irish3.htm
- Searching for Civil Registrations of Births, Deaths & Marriages in Ireland
  www.irishfamilyresearch.co.uk/EssentialResource1.htm
- The General Register Office
  www.welfare.ie/en/Pages/General-Register-Office.aspx
  Click on 'research' for information on obtaining certificates. A page on the 'History of Registration in Ireland' can be accessed from the main page.
- A guide to the General Register Office of Ireland
  http://homepage.eircom.net/~seanjmurphy/gro

- Irish Abroad: Irish Civil Registration / Kyle J. Betit
  www.irishabroad.com/yourroots/expert/civilregistration.asp
- Ireland Civil Registration
  https://familysearch.org/learn/wiki/en/Ireland_Civil_Registration-_Vital_Records
- Irish Civil Registration
  www.irish-genealogy-toolkit.com/Irish-civil-registration.html
- Research Help: Birth/Marriage/Death Index Pages
  www.from-ireland.net/research-help-birth-marriage-death-pages
- Research Help: Civil Records Explanation
  www.from-ireland.net/research-help-civil-records-explanation
- State Registration of Births, Marriages and Deaths
  www.irishtimes.com/ancestor/browse/records/state/index2.htm#GRO
- Research family history at the General Register Office (NI) GRONI
  www.nidirect.gov.uk/index/information-and-services/leisure-home-and-community/family-history-heritage-and-museums/research-family-history-at-the-general-register-office-ni-groni.htm
- Your Family Tree: 25: General Register Office
  www.proni.gov.uk/no.25_-_general_register_of_northern_ireland__100kb_.pdf
  Advice from the Public Record Office of Northern Ireland.
- Northern Ireland civil registration records
  www.irish-genealogy-toolkit.com/Northern-Ireland-civil-registration.html
- Ireland: Superintendent Registrars Districts by County
  www.rootsweb.com/~bifhsusa/irishregnc.html
- Ireland: Civil Registration Districts
  www.irish-genealogy-toolkit.com/Ireland-civil-registration.html
- What's on Irish Certificates
  www.genfindit.com/irlwhatcert.htm
- How to Order B/M/D Certificates
  www.igp-web.com/Waterford/howto.htm
- Ordering Civil Irish (Long Form) Certificates and Photocopies
  www.genfindit.com/ireland.htm
- Film Numbers for L.D.S. Index to their Irish B.D.M. Films
  www.rootsweb.ancestry.com/~fianna/guide/lds-bdm.html
  List of microfilms of civil registration indexes 1864-1921

- Irish Birth Films,
  www.genfindit.com/ibirths.htm
  Civil registration post 1864 at the Latter Day Saints. For marriage films post-1845, visit /imarrs.htm. For death films post 1864, /ideaths.htm

Introductions: Parish Registers
For indexes and databases, see below, p.27-8.
- Irish Church Records
  www.irishtimes.com/ancestor/browse/records/church/index2.htm
  Includes introductory pages for the Church of Ireland, Roman Catholics, Methodists, Presbyterians, Quakers, & Jews.
- Parish Registers - Baptisms, Marriages & Burials, & Other Records, Catholic (Ireland)
  www.genguide.co.uk/source/parish-registers--baptisms-marriages-amp-burials-amp-other-records-catholic-ireland/161
  Explanaton with a detailed bibliography and listing of websites (including databases).
- How to trace family history in Irish church records: Where to start; Where to find records, online and offline
  www.irish-genealogy-toolkit.com/trace-family-history.html
- Genealogy Records: Parish Records and Marriage Licences
  www.nationalarchives.ie/genealogy1/genealogy-records/parish-records-marriage-licences
  The National Archives advice page, with lists of registers held.
- Churches and Searches
  www.rootsweb.ancestry.com/~fianna/county/churches.html
  Searching in church registers.
- Research Help: Irish Church Records Explanation
  www.from-ireland.net/research-help-church-records/
- Parish Registers of the Churches
  http://freepages.genealogy.rootsweb.ancestry.com/~irishancestors/Parish%20registers.html
  Advice page with links.
- Parish Registers in the National Library of Ireland
  www.aughty.org/pdf/nli_familyhist_parishreg.pdf
  General discussion.

- A Guide to Church Records
  www.proni.gov.uk/fww_guide_version_3_july_2014.pdf
  In the Public Record Office of Northern Ireland; covers the Church of Ireland, Methodist, Presbyterian, & Roman Catholic records, etc.
- Frequently Asked Questions: Church Records
  www.proni.gov.uk/no.3_-_church_records__48kb_.pdf
- LDS Film Numbers for Ireland Parish Registers
  http://www.rootsweb.ancestry.com/~fianna/county/ldspars.html
- Church of Ireland Parish Records: Earliest Dates
  http://irelandgenealogyprojects.rootsweb.ancestry.com/Old_IGW/coirecs.html
  Also includes pages for Presbyterians and Roman Catholics
- Church of Ireland Index
  www.proni.gov.uk/index/search_the_archives/online_indexes/church_of_ireland_index.htm
  List of parish registers at the Public Record Office of Northern Ireland.
- Church of Ireland Parishes
  www.rootsweb.ancestry.com/~fianna/county/coirecs.html
  List, with commencement dates of registers.
- Presbyterian Church Records
  www.rootsweb.ancestry.com/~fianna/county/presbrecs.html
  List of registers; commencement dates only.
- Marriage and Burial Records of Irish Presbyterians / Sherry Irvine
  www.ancestralfindings.com/freea7473.htm
- Roman Catholic Records
  www.irishtimes.com/ancestor/browse/counties/rcmaps
  Comprehensive listing of registers for every Irish parish
- Roman Catholic Records Guides
  www.rootsweb.ancestry.com/~fianna/county/parishes.html
  Includes pages for every county.
- Catholic Parish Registers
  www.nli.ie/en/parish-register.aspx
  At the National Library of Ireland. Note that, as this book goes to press, the digitisation of these records has just been completed.
- Roman Catholic Parish Records On Microfilm
  www.from-ireland.net/catholic-parish-records-microfilm
  County pages listing films held by various institutions.

- Irish Catholic Parish Registers on Ancestry.com
  www.ancestry.com/cs/Satellite?childpagename=USLearning Center%2FLearning_C%2FPageDefault&pagename=Learning Wrapper&cid=1265125316989

Introductions: Monumental Inscriptions
- Ireland Cemeteries
  https://familysearch.org/learn/wiki/en/Ireland_Cemeteries
  Advice from the Latter Day Saints.
- Your Family Tree, 21: Guide to Gravestone Inscriptions
  www.proni.gov.uk/no.21_-_gravestone_inscriptions__83kb_.pdf
  See also
  /no.22_-_understanding_the_stones__74kb_.pdf.
  For a list of cemetery records held, see
  /no.27_-_burial_records__93kb_.pdf.
- Cemetary Records
  www.rootsweb.ancestry.com/~fianna/guide/cemetary.html
  Brief introduction.
- Ireland
  www.mbs-brasses.co.uk/page62.html#Ireland
  Bibliography of monumental brasses

National & International Databases & Directories

Civil Registration Databases & Indexes
- Ireland, Civil Registration Indexes, 1845-1958
  https://familysearch.org/search/collection/1921305
  Database.
- Ireland, Deaths, 1864-1870
  https://familysearch.org/search/collection/1584965
  Database.
- 1864 Ireland Birth Index
  www.irelandgenweb.com/BirthIndex
  Index to the 1864 civil registers.

Parish Register Databases, Transcripts, & Indexes
- International Genealogical Index
  https://familysearch.org/search/collection/igi

For an introduction to this massive database of birth & marriage records, visit
https://familysearch.org/learn/wiki/en/International_Genealogical_ Index.

This is an index to microfilm of parish registers etc., which can be borrowed through Family History Centres using the batch numbers listed in:
- Ireland I.G.I. Batch Numbers
  http://freepages.genealogy.rootsweb.ancestry.com/~hughwallis/ IGIBatchNumbers/CountryIreland.htm
- Ireland Births and Baptisms, 1620-1881,
  https://familysearch.org/learn/wiki/en/Ireland_Births_and_ Baptisms_%28FamilySearch_Historical_Records%29
  Over, 5,000,000 entries, although far from complete. A sub-set of the I.G.I.
- Ireland Marriages, 1619-1898
  https://familysearch.org/search/collection/1584964
  Over 430,000 entries. A sub-set of the I.G.I.
- UKBMD: Births, , Marriages, Deaths and Censuses on the Internet
  www.ukbmd.org.uk
  Includes many Irish links.
- Ireland Birth, Marriage & Death, including Parish
  http://search.ancestry.co.uk/Places/Europe/Ireland/Default.aspx? category=34
  Pay per view. Includes indexes to Civil Registration Births & Marriages, 1864-1958, & Deaths, 1864-1958, select Births & Baptisms, 1620-1911 & Marriages, 1619-1898, select Catholic Births and Baptisms, 1763-1912, Marriages, 1742-1912, & Deaths, 1756-1881, etc.
- Irish Life Events (Birth, Marriage, Death) Records
  www.findmypast.ie/articles/world-records/full-list-of-the-irish- family-history-records/life-events-birth-marriage-death? sourceID=13
  Includes both civil and some parish registers. Pay per view.
- Ireland Births and Baptisms, 1620-1881,
  https://familysearch.org/search/collection/1584963
  Includes c.2,800,000 records. For c.425,000 marriages, 1619-1898, see **/1584964**

- Ireland Marriages, 1619-1898
  www.worldvitalrecords.com/indexinfo.aspx?ix=fs_1584964
  Pay per view. Limited coverage.
- The Anglican Record Project
  http://ireland.anglican.org/about/151
  Project to transcribe parish registers from across Ireland. Currently includes transcripts for Delgany (Glendalough), Wicklow, 1666-1900; Bunclody (Newtownbarry) Union, Co. Wexford (including Bunclody/Newtownbarry, 1799-1903, Kilrush 1878-1903, Kidavin/Barragh 1799-1805 & 1830-1903, & Clonegal/Moyacombe, 1792-1906; Templeshanbo, Co. Wexford, marriages 1800-1814; Fermoy Garrison church, Co. Cork, Baptisms, 1920-22; Kilgarvan, Co. Kerry, baptisms 1811-50, marriages 1812-1947, & burials 1819-50 & 1878-1960; Buttevant Garrison, Co. Cork, baptisms 1917-22; Cloghran, Co. Dublin, baptisms 1782-1864, marriages 1739, 1782-1839, & burials 1732-1864; Kilsaran, (Castlebellingham), Co.Louth, baptisms 1818-1840; marriages 1818-1844, & burials 1818-1900; Kenmare, Co. Kerry, marriages 1819-1950; Strabannon, Co. Kerry, baptism 1688-1750, 1765, & 1782-1847, marriages 1698–1754, & 1778–1844, & burials 1698-1751 & 1782-1864; Dromiskin, Co. Louth, baptisms 1791-1839, marriages 1805-1903, & burials 1802–1907; Manfieldstown, Co. Louth, baptisms 1824-1856, marriages 1824-1850, & burials 1838–1884; Derryloran, Co's Londonderry & Tyrone, baptisms, 1796-1896; confirmations, 1824, 1828, 1833, 1837, 1840, 1843, 1846; 1849; 1852; 1856.
- Gen Wed.com Marriage Records Online
  www.genwed.com/UK/ireland.htm
  Links page.
- Ireland Deaths 1864-1870
  www.findmypast.ie/articles/world-records/full-list-of-the-irish-family-history-records/life-events-birth-marriage-death/ireland-deaths-1864-1870
  Pay per view; from civil records.
- Dusty Docs: Ireland
  http://dustydocs.com.au/Country/show/country_id/4
  Gateway.
- Ireland: Births or Baptisms, Deaths & Marriages Exchange
  http://vicki.thauvin.net/chance/ireland/bmd

- Irish Church Records: Baptisms and Marriages
  http://freepages.genealogy.rootsweb.ancestry.com/~irishchurchrecords
  Database with entries contributed by users.
- IGRS Early Irish Marriages database
  http://www.irishancestors.ie/?page_id=1926
- Irishgenealogy.ie. Church Records
  http://churchrecords.irishgenealogy.ie/churchrecords
  Database currently including extensive entries from Carlow, Cork, Dublin, & Kerry.
- Marriages from the Master Marriage Index
  www.ajmorris.com/dig/toc/_000mmi.htm
  Pay per view. Index of marriages overseas.

Monumental Inscriptions Databases, Transcripts, & Indexes
- Ancestors at Rest: Free Cemetery Records Database for the United States, Canada, England, and Ireland.
  http://ancestorsatrest.com/cemetery_records/
  Scroll down for inscriptions from various places: Co.Antrim: Belfast Charitable Institution. Co. Dublin: Blackrock, Castleknock, Tallaght. Co. Meath: Loughcrew, Rathmore. Co. Wexford: Adamstown, Castletown, Cleariestown, Duncormack, Ferns, Gory, Kilmannon, & Rathangan. Co. Wicklow: Barranisky, Ennisboyne, Greenane, Hollywood, Glendalough, & Wicklow.
- Memorials of the Dead
  www.irishfamilyresearch.co.uk/MEMS.HTM
  Subscription required. Originally published by the Association for the Preservation of Memorials of the Dead, late 19th c.
- Find your ancestors in Cantwell's Memorials Of The Dead
  www.findmypast.ie/articles/world-records/full-list-of-the-irish-family-history-records/life-events-birth-marriage-death/cantwells-memorials-of-the-dead
  Pay per view. Over 24,000 inscriptions transcribed by Brian Cantwell, primarily from Co's Wexford & Wicklow, but also Co's Cork, Dublin, Galway, Kildare & Sligo.

- Find a Grave
  www.findagrave.com
  Click on 'Search for a cemetery', and search 'Ireland' for lists of transcriptions from over 3000 Irish cemeteries – far too many to list here. Mostly a small number of entries from each cemetery, but there are some with substantial numbers.
- Headstone Project
  www.igp-web.com/IGPArchives/headstones.htm
  Over 68,000 photogaphs of headstones; many pages listed below.
- Monumental Inscriptions, Cemeteries and Graveyards - Ireland - Main Page
  www.geni.com/projects/Monumental-Inscriptions-Cemeteries-and-Graveyards-Ireland-Main-Page/17634
  Links pages for every county, with some other information.
- Discover Everafter
  www.discovereverafter.com/graveyards
  Index to inscriptions in numerous cemeteries, mainly in Ulster
- Historic Graves
  http://historicgraves.com/
  Transcriptions from over 500 cemeteries, with photographs of tombstones.
- Ireland's Gravestone Index
  https://securec45.ezhostingserver.com/irish-world-com/ gravestones/index.cfm
  Pay per view. Over 400,000 entries from Counties Antrim, Armagh, Donegal, Down, Fermanagh, Londonderry, Louth, Monaghan & Tyrone.
- Irish Gravestone Photographs
  www.from-ireland.net/free-gravestone-photographs
  Includes over 18,000 photographs from cemeteries in Counties Carlow, Clare, Cork, Kerry, Kildare, Kilkenny, Laois, Limerick, Offaly, Roscommon, Tipperary & Wicklow.
- Irish Gravestone Inscriptions
  http://search.ancestry.co.uk/search/db.aspx?dbid=49207
  Pay per view. Mainly from Ulster.
- Irish Gravestone Records
  www.from-ireland.net/free-gravestone-records
  Includes over 70,000 records from cemeteries listed below under counties.
- Genealogy Research Service Ireland: Headstone Inscriptions
  http://homepage.eircom.net/~genbruce/MyGenealogy/Genealogy8. html
  Lists transcripts available in the National Library of Ireland, and in Dublin City Library.
- Find your ancestors in Ireland Memorial and Burial Register, 1618-2005
  www.findmypast.ie/articles/world-records/full-list-of-the-irish-family-history-records/life-events-birth-marriage-death/ireland-memorial-and-burial-register-1618-2005
  Inscriptions database; pay per view.
- Ireland Cemetery Records
  http://interment.net/ireland/index.htm
  Numerous indexes to inscriptions, mostly listed below.
- International Jewish Cemetery Project
  www.iajgsjewishcemeteryproject.org/ireland/index.html
- History from Headstones
  www.historyfromheadstones.com
  Database of 50,000+ Northern Ireland monumental inscriptions.
- Irelands Gravestone Index
  www.irish-world.com/gravestones
  Over 400,000 inscriptions from Co's. Antrim, Armagh, Donegal, Down, Fermanagh, Londonderry, Louth, Monaghan, & Tyrone.
- Irish Gravestone Transcriptions
  www.from-ireland.net/free-gravestone-transcriptions
  Numerous pages of transcriptions, mostly listed below
- Irish Graveyards
  www.irishgraveyards.ie
  Extensive database.
- Irish Memorials of Dead
  www.ajmorris.com/dig/toc/memdead.htm
  Pay per view site. Index to 19th c. published book of tombstone inscriptions.
- Ulster Historical Foundation: Northern Irish Gravestone Inscriptions
  www.ancestryireland.com/family-records/gravestone-inscriptions
  Extensive database, including pre-1900 inscriptions from Antrim, Armagh, Down, Fermanagh, Londonderry, & Tyrone. Indexed at **/graveyards-in-ulster**

- Find your ancestors in Ireland Memorial and Burial Register, 1618-2005
  www.findmypast.ie/articles/world-records/full-list-of-the-irish-family-history-records/life-events-birth-marriage-death/ireland-memorial-and-burial-register-1618-2005
  Pay per view database, with over 41,000 entries from Cavan, Donegal, Fermanagh, Leitrim, Meath, Monaghan & Tyrone.
- Irish Jewish Roots
  www.irishjewishroots.com/names/
  Includes database of 52,000+ births, marriages & deaths.

War Memorials
- Irish War Memorials
  www.irishwarmemorials.ie
  Photographs of numerous war memorials.
- Roll of Honour
  www.warmemorials.org/links-northernireland
  Includes memorials from Northern Ireland.
- Irish War Memorials
  www.irishwarmemorials.ie
  Photographs of numerous war memorials.
- War Memorials Online
  www.warmemorialsonline.org.uk/
  Includes photographs of numerous Irish war memorials.
- War Memorials Trust: War memorials in Northern Ireland
  www.warmemorials.org/links-northernireland/
- War Memorials in Ulster
  www.ulsterwarmemorials.net/
- Ulster Bank War Memorials / Roll of Honour
  http://ulsterbankwarmemorials.blogspot.co.uk

Newspaper Announcements
- Find your ancestors in Farrar's Index To Irish Marriages 1771-1812
  www.findmypast.ie/articles/world-records/full-list-of-the-irish-family-history-records/life-events-birth-marriage-death/farrars-index-to-irish-marriages-1771-1812
  Pay per view.
- Ireland Old News: Irish Death Notice Index
  www.irelandoldnews.com/obits/
  Index of 54,000+ obituaries.

- Irish Index
  www.irishindex.ca
  15,000 birth, marriage and death announcements from *Freeman's journal,* 1817-23
- Irish Marriages, being an Index to the Marriages in *Walker's Hibernian Magazine,* 1771 To 1812
  www.ulsterancestry.com/ShowFreePage.php?id=195.
  Also available (pay per view) at
  http://search.ancestry.co.uk/search/db.aspx?dbid=9141, & at
  www.worldvitalrecords.com/indexinfo.aspx?ix=ia_irishmarriagesbe01farr
- Index to the births , marriages and deaths in *Anthologia Hibernica,* 1793 1794
  www.celticcousins.net/ireland/anthologia_hibernica.htm
- *Northern Standard* BMDs 1839-1847
  www.ancestryireland.com/family-records/northern-standard-bmds-1839-1847/
  Subscription required.
- Find your ancestors in *Quakers Annual Monitor* 1849
  www.findmypast.ie/articles/world-records/full-list-of-the-irish-family-history-records/life-events-birth-marriage-death/quakers-annual-monitor-1849
  Pay per view.
- Irish Marriage Notices in American Newspapers
  www.findmypast.ie/articles/world-records/full-list-of-the-irish-family-history-records/life-events-birth-marriage-death/irish-marriage-notices-in-american-newspapers
  For death notices, see */irish-death-notices-in-american-newspaper.*

County & Local Pages
In general, I have only listed pages covering more than two or three years. From Ireland **www.from-ireland.net** has many pages covering briefer periods. Pages listing specific families, and those which only include selected entries, are excluded. Note that the 'gravestones' pages on Irish Ancestors **www.irishtimes.com/ancestor** county pages are not separately listed here.

Antrim

- Emerald Ancestors
  www.emeraldancestors.com
  Database covering Co's Antrim, Armagh, Down, Fermanagh, Londonderry & Tyrone.
- Antrim Genealogy
  www.from-ireland.net/county-antrim-genealogy
  Includes indexes to some civil registers, & to inscriptions from Aughnahoy, Creggan, Derriaghy, Killycrappin, Lambeg, Layde & Waterfoot; also list of Roman Catholic parish registers on microfilm, etc.
- Ulster Ancestry Free Genealogy Pages
  www.ulsterancestry.com/ua-free-pages.php
  Includes Ardclinis inscriptions, Ballymena burials, 1800-1900, & headstones, Agnes Street, Belfast, War Memorial 1914-18.
- Irish Birth/Baptism Records – Co. Antrim & Co. Down
  www.ancestryireland.com/family-records/birth-and-baptism-records-county-antrim-and-county-down
  Pay per view. For marriages, see **/marriage-records-co-antrim-co-down.** For deaths & burials, see **/death-burial-records-county-antrim-down**
- Co. Antrim Church Records
  www.rootsweb.ancestry.com/~fianna/county/antrim/ant-chur.html
  List of registers for all denominations. Fianna's denominational pages include:
  - Church of Ireland **/antcoi.html**
  - Presbyterian **/antpres.html**
  - Roman Catholic **/antrc.html**
- Antrim Roman Catholic Records
  www.irishtimes.com/ancestor/browse/counties/rcmaps/antrimrc.htm
  Map with list.
- Antrim Cemetery Records
  www.igp-web.com/IGPArchives/ire/antrim/cem.htm
  Includes pages for Ballycarry, Rasharkin, Kells Abbey, & Larne.
- Graveyards and transcripts for Antrim, ordered by civil parish.
  www.irishtimes.com/ancestor/fuses/counties/index.cfm?fuseaction=graveyards&CityCounty=Antrim
  List.

- Antrim Headstone Photos
  www.igp-web.com/IGPArchives/ire/antrim/photos/tombstones/markers.htm
  From Ballintoy, Belfast, Bonamargy, Bushmills, Layd, Cushendun, Dunluce, Killead, Raloo, Milltown, & Muckamore.

Bann Valley *See* **Londonderry**

Belfast

- Belfast City Council: Burial records
  www.belfastcity.gov.uk/community/burialrecords/burialrecords.aspx
  Database of 360,000 records.
- Rosemary Street Church Records, Belfast Ireland
  http://www.ancestorsatrest.com/church_records/rosemary_street_church_ireland.shtml
  Births , 1822-67; Marriages 1811-45.
- Milltown Cemetery, Belfast
  www.ancestryireland.com/family-records/milltown-cemetery-belfast/
  Subscription required. For those purchasing burial plots, 1924-1930, see **/milltown-roman-catholic-cemetery-list-purchasing-burial-plots-1924-1930/**

Carnlough

- St. John's Roman Catholic Graveyard, Carnlough (New section) Co. Antrim
  www.discovereverafter.com/graveyards/89/carnlough-st-johns-rc-graveyard-new-section

Island Magee

- Baptism Records First Presbyterian Islandmagee
  http://freepages.genealogy.rootsweb.ancestry.com/~econnolly/oextracts/oebaptismsim1.html
- [Island Magee]
  http://irishgenealogy.net/antrim/islandm.txt
  Baptisms,, 1829-1983; Marriages, 1819-1892

Monkstown

- Stephen's Local History Pages
  **http://freepages.history.rootsweb.ancestry.com/~stephenbarnes/
  index.htm**
  Includes Monkstown burials, 1878-1953, & inscriptions.

Armagh *See also* Antrim

- Armagh Genealogy
  www.from-ireland.net/county-armagh-genealogy
  Includes indexes to some civil registers, & to inscriptions from Creggan,
  Crossmaglen and Sandy Hill (Knockadrain); also list of Roman Catholic
  parish registers on microfilm, etc.
- Thinking of Genealogy, Ireland: County Armagh
  www.the-e-site.com/irish/countyarmagh.htm
  Includes Presbyterian marriages from Armagh, 1707-28, & inscriptions
  from Acton & Creggan.
- Ulster Ancestry Free Genealogy Pages
  www.ulsterancestry.com/ua-free-pages.php
  Includes Armagh Presbyterian marriages, 1707-1728, Creggan
  Presbyterian inscriptions, Acton Inscriptions, & Tassagh Keady
  inscriptions.
- Co. Armagh Church Records
  www.rootsweb.ancestry.com/~fianna/county/armagh/arm-chur.html
  Fianna's denominational pages include:
    Church of Ireland **/armcoi.html**
    Presbyterian Church **/armpres.html**
    Roman Catholic parishes and dates **/armrc.html**
- Graveyards and transcripts for Armagh, ordered by civil parish
  **www.irishtimes.com/ancestor/fuses/counties/index.cfm?
  fuseaction=graveyards&CityCounty=Armagh**
  List.
- Armagh Guardian births, marriages & deaths, 1844-1852
  **www.ancestryireland.com/family-records/armagh-guardian-births-
  marriages-deaths-1844-1852**
  Subscription required.

Lurgan

- Lurgan Ancestry: Births, Marriages & Deaths Indexes
  www.lurganancestry.com/bmds.htm
- The Cemeteries of Lurgan
  www.lurganancestry.com/gravestones.htm
  Includes inscriptions and photographs from cemeteries at Aghagallon,
  Donaghcloney (Co.Down), Dougher, Kilwarlin, Lurgan, Magheralin,
  Seagoe, Shankill, & Waringstown (Co.Down).

Lynastown

- Lynastown Burial Ground
  www.craigavonhistoricalsociety.org.uk/rev/cooperlynastownburial.html
  Quaker burials

Tartaraghan

- Tartaraghan Old Graveyards, alias the Toby Hole
  www.craigavonhistoricalsociety.org.uk/rev/flemingtartaraghan.html

Carlow

- Carlow Genealogy
  www.from-ireland.net/county-carlow-genealogy
  Includes indexes to some civil registers, to Leighlinbridge baptism
  records, 1783-6 & 1827-8, & to inscriptions from Ballymurphy, Barragh,
  Carlow, Clonegal, Fennagh, & Urglin; also list of Roman Catholic parish
  registers on microfilm.
- Irish Genealogy.ie: Irish Church Records
  http://churchrecords.irishgenealogy.ie/churchrecords
  Index to many Co.Carlow Roman Catholic parish registers.
- Parishes Records Carlow & Laois County: Parish Records in the
  National Library of Ireland
  www.rootsweb.ancestry.com/~irlcar2/parish_02.htm
- County Carlow Church of Ireland Records: earliest dates and source
  locations
  www.rootsweb.ancestry.com/~fianna/county/carlow/carcoi.html
  List with locations.
- County Carlow Roman Catholic Parishes
  www.rootsweb.ancestry.com/~fianna/county/carlow.html
  Lists register held by the Latter Day Saints.

- County Carlow Baptisms / Christening's,
  www.rootsweb.ancestry.com/~irlcar2/Baptisims_Index.htm
  Includes pages for Bagenalstown, Ballon, Baltinglass, Barragh, Borris
  Carlow, Clonegall, Dunleckney, Hacketstown, Killeshin, Leighlinbridge,
  Myshall, Old Leighlin, Rathoe, & Rathvilly.

- Thinking of Genealogy, Ireland: County Carlow
  www.the-e-site.com/irish/countycarlow.htm
  Includes inscriptions from Bennekerry, Hackets Town, Mullawn, Old
  Leighlin, Rathvilly, etc.
- Graveyards and transcripts for Carlow, ordered by civil parish
  www.irishtimes.com/ancestor/fuses/counties/index.cfm?
  fuseaction=graveyards&CityCounty=Carlow
  List.

- County Carlow Cemetery Records, Ireland
  http://interment.net/ireland/carlow.htm
  Includes indexes to inscriptions at Bennekerry, Hacketstown, Mullawn,
  Old Leithlin, Rathvilly, & Tullow.
- County Carlow Gravestone Inscriptions
  www.rootsweb.ancestry.com/~irlcar2/Gravestone_inscriptons_
  Index.htm
  Includes pages for Acaun, Aghade, Ballicopagan, Ballon, Ballykealey,
  Bestfield, Borris, Carlow, Clonagoose, Clonegal, Dunleckney, Grange,
  Haroldstown, Kellistown, Kildavin, Killerrig, Killeshin, Killinane, Kiltealy,
  Kiltennel, Knockaunnarelic, Linkardstown, Lorum, Mullaun, Newgarden,
  Old Leighlin, Rathvilly, Sleaty, Slyguff, St. Mullin's, Templepeter,
  Tinnahinch, Tinryland, & Tullow.
- USA/Canada Gravestone Inscriptions
  www.rootsweb.ancestry.com/~irlcar2/usa_canada.htm
  Commemorating people from Co. Carlow

Dunleckney
- Carlow: Dunleckney Cemetery: Some Tombstone Inscriptions
  www.ajmorris.com/dig/fap/rec/index.htm
  Click on title. Subscription required.

Killeshin
- Gravestone Inscriptions, Killeshin
  http://freepages.family.rootsweb.ancestry.com/~mjbrennan/
  headstones_killeshin.htm
  For index, see **/headstones_killeshin_index.htm**. See also
  /Graveyards_Surnames_index.htm.

Cavan
- Cavan Genealogy
  www.from-ireland.net/county-cavan-genealogy
  Includes indexes to some civil registers, & to inscriptions from
  Templeport; also list of Roman Catholic Parish Records Available On
  Microfilm.
- Co. Cavan, Ireland, Research Site
  http://freepages.genealogy.rootsweb.ancestry.com/~adrian/
  Cavan.htm
  Includes Ashfield baptsisms, 1821-64, Drung baptisms, 1735-1827, &
  listing of Roman Catholic baptismal registers, etc.
- County Cavan: Church of Ireland: Dates and Source Locations
  www.rootsweb.ancestry.com/~fianna/county/cavan/cavcoi.html
- Church of Ireland Records: Directory of Microfilm and Indexed Records
  http://home.wavecable.com/~colin/genuki/CAV/Cofl.htm
  For Co.Cavan.
- County Cavan Parish Registers held at the Representative Church Body
  Library Dublin
  www.igp-web.com/cavan/coi_parishes.html
- Church of Ireland Records
  http://home.wavecable.com/~colin/genuki/CAV/Cofl.htm
  Directory of microfilmed/indexed baptism, marriage and burial registers
  for Co. Cavan.
  For Methodist registers, see **/Methodist.htm.**
  For Presbyterian registers, see **/Presby.htm.**
  For Quaker registers, see **/Quaker.html.**
  For Roman Catholic registers, see **/RC.htm.**
- Listing of Church of Ireland Baptismal Registers for County Cavan
  http://freepages.genealogy.rootsweb.ancestry.com/~adrian/
  Cav_CIB1.htm

- County Cavan Roman Catholic Parishes: Dates and Source Locations
  www.rootsweb.ancestry.com/~fianna/county/cavan/cavrc.html
- Listing of Roman Catholic Baptismal Registers for County Cavan
  http://freepages.genealogy.rootsweb.ancestry.com/~adrian/
  Cav_RCB1.htm
- Graveyards and transcripts for Cavan, ordered by civil parish
  www.irishtimes.com/ancestor/fuses/counties/index.cfm?
  fuseaction=graveyards&CityCounty=Cavan
  List.
- Cavan Headstone Photos
  www.igp-web.com/IGPArchives/ire/cavan/photos/tombstones/
  markers.htm
  Pages from Cootehill, Crosserlough, Denn, Derver, Drumgoon, Drumlane, Glasleck, Killinagh, Kilnaleck, Kingscourt, Maghera, Teampall Chellaigh, & Templeport.
- County Cavan Cemetery Records Ireland
  http://interment.net/ireland/cavan.htm
  Includes indexes to inscriptions from Ballinacree, Derver, Drumlumman, Maghera, Raffony, Mullagh, Teampall Cheallaigh, & Virginia.
- County Cavan Gravestone Inscriptions
  www.rootsweb.ancestry.com/~fianna/county/cavan/cavtomb.html
  List of transcripts.
- Cavan Cemetery Records
  www.igp-web.com/IGPArchives/ire/cavan/cem.htm
  Includes inscriptions from Drung, Kilmore Cathedral & Virginia.

Ballyhaise
- Baillyhaise Cemetery
  http://home.wavecable.com/~colin/genuki/CAV/Castleterra/
  BallyhaiseCemetery.html
  List of family plots.
- Crosserlough Cemetery, Cavan, Ireland
  www.igp-web.com/IGPArchives/ire/cavan/photos/tombstones/
  1headstones/crosserlough.txt
  See also **/cavan-crosserlough2/index.html**

Bawnboy
- Bawnboy & Templeport Local Genealogical & Historical Data
  www.bawnboy.com/local-genealogy
  Includes Bawnboy inscriptions; Corlough inscriptions; Kilnavert inscriptions; Templeport Anglican baptisms, 1873-1920; Templeport Catholic burials 1827- present; Templeport, Anglican burials 1910 - present; St Mogue's Island, Templeport Lake Graveyard Burial Register 1936-2008 & inscriptions; Templeport inscriptions.

Corlough See Bawnboy

Enniskeen
- Deaths in Roman Catholic Parish of Enniskeen, Kingscourt, County Cavan, Ireland
  www.rootsweb.ancestry.com/~irlcav2/enniskeen-deaths.html
  For Enniskeen 1846-50, and Kingscourt 1848-50.

Killeshandra
- Inscriptions in Killeshandra Old Cemetery
  http://homepages.iol.ie/~galwill/histtomb.htm

Kilnaleck
- St. Mary's, Ballynarry, Kilnaleck, County Cavan, Ireland
  www.igp-web.com/IGPArchives/ire/cavan/photos/tombstones/
  1headstones/ballynarry.txt

Kilnavart See Bawnboy

Knocktemple
- Knocktemple Old Cemetery Inscriptions, County Cavan, Ireland
  http://search.ancestry.com/search/db.aspx?dbid=4225

Templeport See Bawnboy

Clare

- Clare Genealogy
  www.from-ireland.net/county-clare-genealogy
  Includes indexes to some civil registers, to Kilnasoolagh baptisms, 1785-93, & to inscriptions from Ballyvaughan, Bodyke, Broadford, Clonlara, Clooney South, Coad, Corofin, Kilbane, Kilcorcoran, Kildeema, Kilfarboy, Kilfenora, Killaspuglonane, Killenagh, Killernan, Killinaboy, Killinure, Kilmacrehy, Kilmurry, Ibrickane, Kilshanny, Kiltenanlea, Kilvoydan, Lisdoonvarna, Miltown Malbay, Noughaval, Rath, Tooclath & Tulla. Also Roman Catholic parish registers on microfilm, etc.
- Thinking of Genealogy, Ireland: Co. Clare
  www.the-e-site.com/irish/countyclare.htm
  Includes inscriptions from Ballard, Clohanes, Doonbeg, & Drumcliffe, etc.
- Parishes and Church Records
  www.clarelibrary.ie/eolas/coclare/genealogy/parishes.htm
  List of Clare parishes and registers.
- Donated Material: Births/Baptisms, Marriages, Deaths,
  **www.clarelibrary.ie/eolas/coclare/genealogy/don_tran/bmd/
  index_bmd.htm**
  Collection of miscellaneous records.
- County Clare Church of Ireland Parish Records
  www.rootsweb.ancestry.com/~fianna/county/clare/clacoi.html
- County Clare Church of Ireland Parish Registers
  www.genuki.org.uk/big/irl/CLA/COIrecordsi.html
  List of parishes & earliest dates of registers. For Roman Catholic registers, see /RCrecords.htm.
- County Clare Roman Catholic Records
  www.rootsweb.ancestry.com/~fianna/county/clare/clacoi.html
- Assorted Co. Clare Marriages August 1851-June 1862
  www.connorsgenealogy.com/clare/ClareMarriages.htm
- Graveyards and transcripts for Clare, ordered by civil parish.
  **www.irishtimes.com/ancestor/fuses/counties/index.cfm?
  fuseaction=graveyards&CityCounty=Clare**
  List.
- Association for the Preservation of the Memorials of the Dead, Ireland, Journals 1888-1916
  www.clarelibrary.ie/eolas/coclare/genealogy/memorials/index.htm
  Inscriptions from Co. Clare

- Clare Cemetery Records
  www.igp-web.com/IGPArchives/ire/clare/cem.htm
  Includes pages from Clare, Corrovorron, Dromcliffe, Dysart, Ennis Abbey, Ennistymon, Feakle, Inagh, Killernan, Kilnaboy, Lahinch, Moughna, Mullagh, Quin, & Tulla, etc.
- County Clare Cemetery Records, Ireland
  http://interment.net/ireland/clare.htm
  Includes indexes to inscriptions from Ballard, Breffa, Callura, Doolin, Doonbeg, Drumcliffe, Ennistymon, Inagh, Kilfarboy, Killernan, Killofin, Kilmacreehy, Kilmaley, Kilmurry, Kilnamona, Kilrush, Kilshanny, Liscannor, Moughna, Moy, Shanakyle & Tulla.
- Donated Material: Graveyard Inscriptions
  **www.clarelibrary.ie/eolas/coclare/genealogy/don_tran/graves/
  index_graves_main.htm**
  Pages for graveyards at Ballynacally (Clondagad), Broadford, Carrigaholt, Clarecastle, Clonrush, Cross/Kilballyowen, Crusheen, Doonbeg, Doora/Barefield, Dysert, Ennis, Feakle, Kildysert, Kilfiddane, Kilfinaghta, Kilkee, Killaloe, Killeenadeema (Co Galway), Killimer, Kilmacduane, Kilmaley, Kilmanaheen, Kilmihil, Kilmurry Clonderlaw, Kilmurry Ibrickan, Kilmurry McMahon, Kilnoe, Kilrush, Miltown Malbay, Moynoe, Newmarket-on-Fergus, O'Callaghan's Mills, Ogonnelloe, Scarriff, Sixmilebridge, & Tubber (Kilkeedy) .

Ennis

- Ennis Parish: Marriage & Baptism Register
  www.ennisparish.com/genealogy
  Baptisms 1836-1969; marriages 1823-1985.

Inchicronan

- County Clare, Inchicronan Parish, Sranagalloon: Baptisms 1860-1880
  www.connorsgenealogy.com/clare/Sranagalloon.htm

Killard

- Co. Clare Baptisms: Killard/Kilrush/Kilmurry/Kilmacduane
  **http://freepages.genealogy.rootsweb.ancestry.com/~msjenkins/
  records/clarebap.htm**
  Killard and Doonbeg, 1855-80; Kilrush, 1827-80; Kilmurry Ibricken, 1839-80.

Kilmihil

- Kilmihil Community Development: Baptism, Deaths, Graveyard and Marriage Registers
  http://kilmihil-community.com/index.php/kilmihil-history-and-geneology/2-uncategorised/117-baptism-deaths-graveyard-and-marriage-registers
  Indexes.

Kilrush

- Register of Marriages: St. Senan's, Kilrush, Co. Clare, 1829-1906
  http://freepages.genealogy.rootsweb.ancestry.com/~msjenkins/records/stsenan-m.htm

Cork

- Cork Genealogy
  http://www.from-ireland.net/county-cork-genealogy/
  Includes indexes to some civil registers, to Traction Abbey baptisms, 1860-64, & to inscriptions from Adrigole, Aghinagh, Ballycurrany, Bantry, Carrigrohanbeg, Clonmult, Dangandonovan, Desertmore, Glengarriff, Kilcaskin, Kilcrea, Killeagh, Kilnaglory, & Tisaxon, etc.
- County Cork Civil Registrations
  http://freepages.genealogy.rootsweb.ancestry.com/~mturner/cork/a_civil.htm
  Many pages of indexes to and extracts from civil registration for particular places
- The Church of Ireland Parish Register Collections for Cork
  www.corkrecords.com/registers.htm
  Detailed listing, including transcripts from the City of Cork: St Anne Shandon baptisms, 1805-1827 & 1835-1843, marriages 1797-1829, & burials 1854-1864; St Luke marriages 1837-1845; Foundling Hospital baptisms 1818-43 & marriages 1811-1822; St Mary Shandon 1804-1849; Holy Trinity (Christ Church); baptisms, marriages & burials 1643-1660; Cork Cathedral baptisms & marriages (extracts) 1753-1832; St Michael, Blackrock burials 1833-1837; St Nicholas marriages 1790 - 1845.

Also Abbeymahon baptisms 1827-73; Aghabullog, baptisms 1808-1877, marriages 1808-1843 & burials 1809-1879; Ballymartle, Cork: Baptisms 1799-1868. Burials 1800-76; Ballymodan baptisms 1800-64, marriages 1695-1795 (indexes, plus some later extracts); Ballyvourney marriages 1845-1935; Bandon marriages 1847-1862, etc; Berehaven baptisms, marriages, & burials 1787-1842; Buttevant Garrison baptisms 1917-22; Caheragh: baptisms 1798-1913, marriages 1823-1895, & burials 1778-1947; Cape Clear Island marriages 1856-1893; Carrigaline: baptisms 1848-70, marriages 1726-53 & 1791-2; Carrigtwohill baptisms, 1776-1844 & 1863-77, marriages 1779-1844, & burials 1776-1843; Clonmel registers from 1838; Cloyne registers from 1788; Desertserges baptisms 1811-1814, marriages 1812-45, & burials 1849-1872; Drimoleague baptisms & marriages 1802-11, & baptisms: 1812-44; Dunmanaway from 1640; Durras baptisms 1672-1890, & marriages 1688-1940; Dunderrow, Cork baptisms 1805-6 & marriages 1806-18; Fanlobbus baptisms 1855-71 & burials 1855-72; Glengariff baptisms 1863-1913 & marriages 1864-1955; Killeagh baptisms 1782-1880, marriages 1776-1879, & burials 1782-1884; Killowen baptisms 1833-1874; Killowen & Desertserges burials 1851-71; Kilmocomogue marriages 1665-1931; Kilshannig baptisms, from 1731; Kinniegh: baptisms 1795-1854; Lislee baptisms 1809-62, marriages 1809-44 & burials 1825-61; Macroom baptisms 1727-1837, marriages 1736-1835, & burials 1727-1836; Mogeesha baptisms 1852-75; Magourney baptisms 1757-1876, marriages 1756-1844, & burials 1758-1876; Midleton baptisms, marriages & burials 1809-1883; Kinsale marriages & burials 1680-1696; Murragh: baptisms, marriages, & burials 1750-1876; Rathclaren: marriages (index only) 1782-1849; Ross: baptisms, marriages, & burials 1691-1821; Templemartin baptisms 1845-64 & 1871-4; Timoleague baptisms 1823-31, marriages 1823-80, & burials 1823-1870; Youghal register 1665-9.

Also images of original registers for Aghada births, marriages & burials 1805-1817, & marriages 1845-1915; Ballyclough baptisms, 1831-1900, marriages 1831-1848 & burials 1831-99; Castletownroche baptisms, marriages & burials 1728-1803; Corkbeg marriages 1847-1920; Inch marriages 1847-1924; Kilmahon marriages 1852-61; Killanully baptisms 1831-74, & burials 1836-1877; Lislee (Courtmacsherry) baptisms 1822-1825, marriages 1823-4, & burials 1823-1824; also baptisms 1727-1837, marriages 1809-44, & burials 1833-89; Macroom baptisms 1727-1837, marriages 1736-1835, & burials 1727-1836; Mallow baptisms, marriages, & burials 1780-1862; Nohaval baptisms 1846-70, & burials 1849-75; Youghal burials 1865-9.

- County Cork: Church And Parish Records
  http://freepages.genealogy.rootsweb.ancestry.com/~mturner/ cork/_churches.htm
  Includes Ballyhay christenings, 1727-1825; Ballyvourney baptisms, 1810-24, St. Patrick's, Cork, baptisms, 1837-79 & marriages 1835-49 & 1861; Currow baptisms, 1801-3; Drishane & Ballincuslane deaths 1864-9; various Dunmanway vital events; Inchigeelagh baptisms, 1816–1900, & marriages 1816-1900; Kilmicahel baptisms 1821-1851, & marriages 1819-1855, Kilmurry baptisms, 1786-1812, & marriages 1803-1805; many other brief extracts.
- Irish Genealogy.ie: Irish Church Records
  http://churchrecords.irishgenealogy.ie/churchrecords
  Index to many Co.Cork Roman Catholic parish registers.
- County Cork Church of Ireland Records
  www.rootsweb.ancestry.com/~fianna/county/cork/corcoi.html
  Commencement dates only. For Roman Catholic records, see
  /corpres.html.
- McDonnell's Index of Births, Deaths and Marriages
  www.corkpastandpresent.ie/genealogy/mcdonellsindexof birthsdeathsandmarriages
  Mainly from *The Constitution*, or *Cork Advertiser* for 1828.
- Graveyards and transcripts for Cork, ordered by civil parish.
  www.irishtimes.com/ancestor/fuses/counties/index.cfm? fuseaction=graveyards&CityCounty=Cork
  List.
- Cork Graveyards and Published Transcriptions
  http://freepages.genealogy.rootsweb.ancestry.com/~colin/ Ireland/CorkGraveyards.htm
  List.
- County Cork Cemetery Records, Ireland
  http://interment.net/ireland/cork.htm
  Includes index to inscriptions from the British Military Graveyard at Ballincollig.

- County Cork Cemeteries and Gravestones
  http://freepages.genealogy.rootsweb.ancestry.com/~mturner/ cork/a_cemetery.htm
  Includes inscriptions from Berehaven, Churchtown, Dangandonovan, Doneraile, Killabraher, Kilbrogran, Killeigh, Liscarroll, Mallow, Murrisk, and many other places.
- Fáilte Romhat
  www.failteromhat.com
  Click on 'Cemetery transcriptions' for inscriptions from Ardfield Castleventry, Clonakilty, Inchydoney, Kilgarriff, Killkerranmore, Kilnagross, Rathbary, & Rosscarbery.
- Historic Graves
  http://historicgraves.com/
  Includes inscriptions from 129 Co Cork graveyards.
- [Gravestones from various Cemeteries in West Cork]
  www.ginnisw.com/Graves/Thumb/Thumbs1.htm

Ahiohill See Murragh

Ballincollig
- Ballincollig Marriages 1864-1960, Co. Cork
  http://freepages.genealogy.rootsweb.ancestry.com/~mturner/ cork/ballingcollig_m.htm

Ballyneen
- Ballyneen District Deaths by Surname
  www.ginnisw.com/Ballineen%20District%20Deaths.html
  From the civil registers; covers 1864 70.

Bandon
- The Church Records which exist of the Parishes of Bandon and the Surrounding Area
  www.bandon-genealogy.com/parish_records.htm
  See also **/Churches.htm.**

Castletown
- [Gravestones from Castletown and Kinneigh, County Cork]
  www.ginnisw.com/Ireland%20Trip%202001/Kinneigh%20and% 20Castletown%20Graves/Thumb/Thumbs1.htm

Cork

- Register of the Parish of the Holy Trinity (Christ Church), Cork, From July, 1643, To February, 1668
www.worldvitalrecords.com/indexinfo.aspx?ix=ia_registerofparish00holy
Pay per view. From a printed book.

Enniskeane

- Catholic Baptisms Enniskeane, Co. Cork,,
www.ginnisw.com/Baptisms%20from%20Enniskeane%20RC%20records.htm
Index, mid-19th c. For marriages, 1815-1932, see
/Enniskeane%20RC%20Marriages.htm.
- Deaths from Enniskeane Parish Register and Ahiohill Cemetery
www.ginnisw.com/Deaths%20Enniskeane%20Ahiohill.htm

Kinneigh

- Kinneigh Parish Records 1795-1854
www.paulturner.ca/Ireland/Cork/Kinneigh_Parish/kinneigh-parish-text-1.htm
- Abbeylands Cemetery, Kinsale
www.findagrave.com

Midleton

- [Gravestones from Midleton, Co. Cork]
www.ginnisw.com/Ireland%20Trip%202001/Midleton%20Graves/Thumb/Thumbs1.htm

Murragh

- [Gravestones from Old Murragh Cemetery and Ahiohill Cemetery]
www.ginnisw.com/Ireland%20Trip%202001/Murragh%20and%20Ahiohill%20Cemetery/Thumb/Thumbs1.htm

Donegal

- Donegal Genealogy
www.from-ireland.net/county-donegal-genealogy
Includes indexes to some civil registers, & to Donaghmore baptisms, 1840-45; also list of Roman Catholic Parish registers on microfilm.

- Ulster Ancestry Free Genealogy Pages
www.ulsterancestry.com/ua-free-pages.php
Includes Assaroe Abbey Cemetery, Ballyshannon inscriptions , etc.
- Donegal Genealogy Resources: Birth, Marriage and Death Records
http://freepages.genealogy.rootsweb.ancestry.com/~donegal
Includes index to civil birth registrations, 1864; Ballintra baptisms 1866-1913, & marriages 1866-1945; Church Hill civil registrations, 1864-1881; Cloncha births, 1669 to 1783; Clondavaddog marriage index, 1847 to 1865; Crossroads, Dunfanaghy and Gweedore civil birth registrations (selected) 1864-1899; Dunfanaghy baptism index; Dungloe civil marriage registrations, 1864–1870; Gartan banns & marriages 1853-80+; Glenswilly marriage banns 1853–1857, & Civil Birth Registrations, 1864–1881; Gweedore births, & baptisms index; Iskaheen baptism index, 1858-1901; Kilmacrenan baptisms index, late 19th c., marriages, 1853-67, banns, 1853–1857, & civil birth registrations, 1864-81; Letterkenny banns, 1853-1857; Malin Head baptisms, late 19th c.; Rathmelton baptism index, late 19th c. (in progress).
- County Donegal Church of Ireland Records
www.rootsweb.ancestry.com/~fianna/county/donegal/doncoi.html
List with locations. For other denominations, see:
Methodists **/donmeth.html**
Presbyterians **/donpres.html**
Roman Catholics **/donrc.html**
- Graveyards and transcripts for Donegal, ordered by civil parish.
www.irishtimes.com/ancestor/fuses/counties/index.cfm?fuseaction=graveyards&CityCounty=Donegal
List.
- Cemeteries of Donegal
freepages.genealogy.rootsweb.com/~donegaleire/Cemeteries.html
Many pages, including some photographs.
- County Donegal Memorial Records
http://www.rootsweb.ancestry.com/~fianna/county/donegal/dontomb.html
Location of transcripts.
- County Donegal Cemetery Records, Ireland
http://interment.net/ireland/donegal.htm
Includes indexes to inscriptions from Ballyshannon, Finner, Gartan, & Kilteevogue.

- Find your ancestors in Donegal Cemetery Records
  www.findmypast.ie/articles/world-records/full-list-of-the-irish-family-history-records/life-events-birth-marriage-death/donegal-cemetery-records
- Online Headstone Inscriptions, Co Donegal
  http://freepages.genealogy.rootsweb.ancestry.com/~donegal/mis.htm
  Includes separate pages for graveyards and cemeteries at Annagar, Arranmore, Assaroe, Balleeghan, Ballybogan, Ballybrack, Ballyshannon, Bruckless, Burt, Allsaints, Kilmacrenan, Clonca, Clonleigh, Cloon, Cockhill, Convoy, Culdaff, Doe Castle, Doe, Donaghmore, Drumhaggart, Drumkeen, Drung, Dungloe, Edenfinfreagh, Fanavolty, Finner, Fintown, Frosses, Gartan, Glencolumbkille, Glenswilly, Glenties, Gortahork, Grange, Inch, Inver, Iskaheen, Kilcar, Kill, Killaghtee, Killea, Killybegs Upper, Kilmacrenan, Kilmonaster, Kilrean, Kilteevoge, Kincasslagh, Lag, Leck, Magheragallon, Malin, Massmount, Mevagh, Moress, Moville, Muff, Murlog, New Glenties, Rathmullen Priory, Raymoghy, Redcastle, St Johnston, Strahack, Straid, Stranorlar, Taughboyne, Templecrone, Templedouglas, Toome, Tory Island, Trenta, Tullaghobegley, Tully, Tullyaughnish, & Umlagh.

Belcruit *see* Templecrone

Carne *See* Pettigo

Clonmany
- Roman Catholic Marriages for the parish of Clonmany (1852-1900)
  www.iol.ie/~inishowen/genealogy/records/Clonmany/Marriage/index.html

Conaghan *see* Templecrone

Conwal
- Conwal, County Donegal Resources
  http://freepages.genealogy.rootsweb.ancestry.com/~donegal/Conwalproj.htm
  Includes Conwal & Leck (St. Eunan's Letterkenny) Roman Catholic Baptisms 1853-62, Glenswilly RC Baptisms Oct 1874 - 31 Mar 1881,

Birth, Marriage & Death Notices, Conwal Co Donegal, 1829-56, transcribed from the *Londonderry Sentinel* 1829-69, Civil Birth Registrations, Conwal Parish, Co Donegal 1864-1881, St Eunan's Marriage Banns, Letterkenny, Co Donegal, etc.

Creeslough
- Creeslough Cemetery
  http://freepages.genealogy.rootsweb.ancestry.com/~donegaleire/Doncem.html

Crossroads
- Crossroads Presbyterian Church, County Donegal, Ireland: Church Records
  http://mcn.ie/crossroads/genealogy/intro.html
  Births, from 1811, deaths 1854-95, marriages, 19-20th c.

Dungloe *See* Templecrone

Edenfinfreagh *See* Inishkeel

Finner
- Find your ancestors in Donegal Cemetery Records
  www.findmypast.ie/articles/world-records/full-list-of-the-irish-family-history-records/life-events-birth-marriage-death/donegal-cemetery-records
  Pay per view. Inscriptions from Finner.

Fintown *See* Inishkeel

Gartan *See* Termon

Glencolumbkille
- Marriage & Death Notices, Glencolumbkille, Co Donegal, 1832 to 1869, transcribed from the *Strabane Morning Post*, *Londonderry Standard* & *Londonderry Sentinel* 1829-69
  http://freepages.genealogy.rootsweb.ancestry.com/~donegal/glencolumbbmdnotices.htm

Glenties *See also* Inishkeel
- St. Connell's, Glenties, Baptisms, Oct. 1866-Jan 1870.
  **http://freepages.genealogy.rootsweb.ancestry.com/~donegal/
  fintownreg.htm**

Golan *See* Kilmacrenan

Inishkeel
- Inishkeel, Donegal Resources
  **http://freepages.genealogy.rootsweb.ancestry.com/~donegal/
  inishkeelproj.htm**
  Includes inscriptions from Edenfinfreagh, Fintown, Glenties, &
  Kilclooney,

Kilclooney *See* Inishkeel

Killeshandra
- Inscriptions in Killeshandra Old Cemetery
  www.iol.ie/~galwill/histtomb.htm

Kilteevoge *See also Cloghan*
- Kilteevoge Marriages 1855-1880
  **http://freepages.genealogy.rootsweb.ancestry.com/~donegal/
  kilteevogemarr.htm**

Leck *see* Conwal

Lettermacaward *see also* Toome
- Lettermacaward, Co. Donegal Resources
  **http://freepages.genealogy.rootsweb.ancestry.com/~donegal/
  lettermacproj.htm**
  Includes births 1864-1909, civil marriage registrations 1864 to 1870,
  non-Catholic marriages 1845-63, & civil death registrations 1864-70.

Moville
- Moville Records: Roman Catholic Parish Records
  www.movillerecords.com/parish.htm
  Covers 1847-66.

Pettigo
- Carne Graveyard, Pettigo, Co. Donegal
  **www.rootsweb.com/~nirfer2/Documents/Cemeteries/
  Carne_Cemetery_1.doc**

Raphoe
- Union of Strabane Death Index ... Deaths Registered in the District of
  Raphoe
  **http://freepages.genealogy.rootsweb.ancestry.com/~donegaleire/
  Raphdeath.html**

  For 1866-7.

Taughboyne
- Taughboyne death announcements, transcribed from the Londonderry
  Sentinel 1829-69
  **http://freepages.genealogy.rootsweb.ancestry.com/~donegal/
  taudthannounce.htm**

Taughboyne Union
- Taughboyne Union Registers 1820–1900
  http://ireland.anglican.org/about/189

Templecrone
- Templecrone, Co. Donegal, Resources
  **http://freepages.genealogy.rootsweb.ancestry.com/~donegal/
  dunaugullies.htm**
  Includes Templecrone births, marriages & deaths from various civil &
  parish registers, & from newspapers; also Belcruit marriages, 1878-84,
  Conaghan Births 1864-1907; Dungloe District births, 1864-81 & deaths,
  1864-70.

Termon
- St. Columba's Church, Termon & Gartan
  **http://freepages.genealogy.rootsweb.ancestry.com/~donegal/
  gartan/termongartan.htm**

Tullaghobegly

- Tullaghobegly, Co. Donegal Resources
  **http://freepages.genealogy.rootsweb.ancestry.com/~donegal/
  tullaghoproject.htm**
  Includes civil births, 1864-81 (incomplete), births in the Crossroads/Gweedore/Dunfanaghy Districts, Roman Catholic baptisms 1849-1861, Old St. Mary's Church, Held at Christ the King Church (Gortahork), Master index to online Gweedore births and baptisms, marriages in the Dunfanaghy Registrar's District 1864 to 1880, Roman Catholic Gweedore marriages, 1855-1916, Marriages at St Mary's Tullaghobegly/Gweedore 1866-76, deaths in the Dunfanaghy Registrar's District 1864-1921, & burials 1849-1863, Old St. Mary's Church, Held at Christ the King Church (Gortahork). Also headstone inscriptions from Gortahork, Magheragallon, Killult, Tory Island, & Tullaghobegley.

Down *see also* Antrim

- Down Genealogy
  www.from-ireland.net/county-down-genealogy/
  Includes indexes to some civil registers, Clonallen marriages, 1826-28, Kilkeel baptisms, 1845-62, & to inscriptions from Balieysmill, Boardsmills, Dundonald, Killaney, Killybawn, Knockbreda and Legacurry; also list of Roman Catholic parish registers on microfilm.
- Ulster Ancestry Free Genealogy Pages
  www.ulsterancestry.com/ua-free-pages.php
  Includes Donaghcloney inscriptions, & Banbridge war memorial..
- Churches and graveyards of Co. Down
  **http://freepages.genealogy.rootsweb.ancestry.com/~rosdavies/
  CHURCHES/A-I.htm#Aghaderg**
  List of locations, cemeteries, & some records.
- County Down Church of Ireland Parish Records
  www.rootsweb.ancestry.com/~fianna/county/down/dowcoi.html
- County Down Presbyterian Records
  www.rootsweb.ancestry.com/~fianna/county/down/dowpres.html
- County Down Roman Catholic Records
  www.rootsweb.ancestry.com/~fianna/county/down/dowrc.html
- County Down Births, 1865-1875,
  http://countydown.x10.mx/html/index2.htm

- Graveyards and transcripts for Down, ordered by civil parish
  **www.irishtimes.com/ancestor/fuses/counties/index.cfm?
  fuseaction=graveyards&CityCounty=Down**
  List.
- Thinking of Genealogy, Ireland, County Down
  www.the-e-site.com/irish/countydown.htm
  Includes Ardglass & Ballooley inscriptions, Inch burials, 18-19th c.; Kilkeel births, late 19th c.; etc.
- County Down Memorials
  www.rootsweb.ancestry.com/~fianna/county/down/dowtomb.html
  List of transcripts.
- Down Cemetery Records
  www.igp-web.com/IGPArchives/ire/down/cem.htm
  Includes pages from Balligan, Clonmallon, Donaghadee, Donaghmore, Downpatrick, Drumbeg, Hillsborough, Kilmegan, Magheradrool, & Seapatrick.
- Published gravestone inscriptions for County Down
  www.presbyterianhistoryireland.com/index.php?id=gravestones
  Presbyterian graveyards.
- Gravestones
  www.bangor.homecall.co.uk/index.htm
  Includes inscriptions from Ballycopeland, Ballywalter, Bangor, Donaghadee, Greyabbey Millisle, Templepatrick, & Whitechurch
- Down Headstone Photos
  **www.igp-web.com/IGPArchives/ire/down/photos/tombstones/
  markers.htm**
  Includes pages for Dundonald, Hillsborough, Hollywood, Killinchy, Killyleagh, Knockbreda, & Movilla, etc.
- Churches and Graveyards of Co. Down
  **http://freepages.genealogy.rootsweb.ancestry.com/~rosdavies/
  CHURCHES/A-I.htm**
  Continued at /K_W.htm.
  List.

Aghlisnafin

- Selected Tombstone Inscriptions from Aghlisnafin, County Down
  www.ajmorris.com/dig/fap/rec
  Registration needed. Click on title.

Anaghlone

- Find your ancestors in Ireland Down Anaghlone Presbyterian Baptisms 1839-1913,
  www.findmypast.ie/articles/world-records/full-list-of-the-irish-family-history-records/life-events-birth-marriage-death/ireland-down-anaghlone-presbyterian-baptisms-1839-1913
  Pay per view. For marriages, 1845-1913, see
  /ireland-down-anaghlone-presbyterian-marriages-1845-1913

Annaclone

- Find your ancestors in Ireland Down Annaclone (CoI) Baptisms 1877-1900
  www.findmypast.ie/articles/world-records/full-list-of-the-irish-family-history-records/life-events-birth-marriage-death/ireland-down-annaclone-coi-baptisms-1877-1900
  For marriages, 1845-1900, see /ireland-down-annaclone-coi-marriages-1845-1900; for burials, 1877-1900,
  see /ireland-down-annaclone-coi-burials-1877-1900.
- Find your ancestors in Ireland Down St Colmans Annaclone (RC) Baptisms 1834-1913
  www.findmypast.ie/articles/world-records/full-list-of-the-irish-family-history-records/life-events-birth-marriage-death/ireland-down-st-colmans-annaclone-rc-baptisms-1834-1913
  Pay per view. For marriages, 1851-1913, see /ireland-down-st-colmans-annaclone-rc-marriages-1851-1913; for burials 1851-1913,
  see /ireland-down-st-colmans-annaclone-rc-burials-1851-1913

Ballynahinch

- Ballynahinch Presbyterian Church Registers; includes Dromara, Kilmore & Clough (Drumca) churches: Baptismal Register 1696-1735
  http://freepages.genealogy.rootsweb.ancestry.com/~rosdavies/WORDS/BallynahinchPresbyterianBirths.htm
  For marriages, 1696-1733, see
  /BallynahinchPresbyterianMarriages.htm

Ballyroney

- Find your ancestors in Ireland Down Ballyroney Presbyterian Baptisms, 1819-1913,
  www.findmypast.ie/articles/world-records/full-list-of-the-irish-family-history-records/life-events-birth-marriage-death/ireland-down-ballyroney-presbyterian-baptisms-1819-1913
  Pay per view. For marriages, 1831-1906, see
  /ireland-down-ballyroney-presbyterian-marriages-1831-1906.

Banbridge

- Marriage Register of the Presbyterian Congregation of Banbridge, County Down, 1756-1794
  http://freepages.genealogy.rootsweb.ancestry.com/~donaghmore1/banmarreg.html
  Also available at:
  http://freepages.genealogy.rootsweb.ancestry.com/~jeanmccarthy36/old_marriage_records.htm
- Banbridge Area, Co. Down Marriages: some Presbyterian Marriages 1848-1864
  http://freepages.genealogy.rootsweb.ancestry.com/~donaghmore1/banprmar.html

Donaghmore

- Donaghmore Register of Baptisms 1804-1900,
  http://freepages.genealogy.rootsweb.ancestry.com/~donaghmore1/donaghmore/donvrbapt1.html
  For marriages, 1846-1900, see /donvrmar1.html; for Presbyterian inscriptions, see /donpregraverec.html
- Birth, Marriage & Death Notices, Donaghmore, Co Donegal, 1829 to 1856, transcribed from the *Strabane Morning Post*, *Londonderry Standard* & *Londonderry Sentinel*
  http://freepages.genealogy.rootsweb.ancestry.com/~donegal/donaghmorebmdnotices.htm
- Glascar Presbyterian Church Records, Glaskermore, Donaghmore Parish
  http://freepages.genealogy.rootsweb.ancestry.com/~donaghmore1/donaghmore/glascarprch.html 1781-1832

Glaskermore see Donaghmore

Inch
- Search Inch Parish Records 1788-1872, Ireland
  **www.ancestorsatrest.com/church_records/inch_parish_records_
  burials.sht**ml
  Burials only, to 1856 at present.

Kilkeel
- Kilkeel Parish Marriages and Births,
  **http://countydown.x10.mx/html/kilkeel,marriages%20and%
  20births.htm**
  Mid-19th c.

Lower Mourne
- Lower Mourne (Ballymartin & Glassdrumman) Marriages, 1839-1849
  **www.igp-web.com/IGPArchives/ire/down/churches/lower-mourne-
  mar01.txt**

  For 1850-60, see **/lower-mourne-mar02.txt**

Newry
- Partial Newry Marriage & Baptism Records from L.D.S. Microfilm
  **http://freepages.genealogy.rootsweb.ancestry.com/~
  donaghmore1/newrymarbap.html For c.1784-1820.**

Dublin
- Irish Genealogy.ie: Irish Church Records
  http://churchrecords.irishgenealogy.ie/churchrecords
  Index to many Co.Dublin Church of Ireland, Roman Catholic, &
  Presbyterian parish registers.
- Dublin Genealogy
  www.from-ireland.net/county-dublin-genealogy
  Includes indexes to some civil registers, Baldoyle, Howth and Kinsealy
  baptisms, 1784-1800, list of surnames in St. Thomas', Dublin, parish
  register, 1750-91, & inscriptions from Deansgrange, Glasnevin, St.
  Andrew's and Taney, etc.
- County Dublin: Church of Ireland Records
  www.rootsweb.com/~fianna/county/dublin/dubcoi.html
  List with locations. For other denominatins, see:
  Other Protestant Records **/dubprot.html**
  Roman Catholics **/dubrc.html**

- Dublin Heritage: Parish Record
  www.dublinheritage.ie/parish_records/index.html
  Details of database of births, marriages and burials for Dublin.
- Dublin City Library and Archive: Dublin Graveyards Directory
  http://dublinheritage.ie/graveyards
- Dublin Cemetery Records
  www.igp-web.com/IGPArchives/ire/dublin/cem.htm
  Includes list of Dublin Cemeteries, and pages of monumental
  inscriptions from Baldoyle, Ballyboghil, Blackrock, Castleknock,
  Colmanstown, Crumlin, Dolphin's Barn, Donabate, Donnybrook,
  Drimnagh, Drumcondra, Dublin (many), Esker, Finglas, Glasnevin,
  Irishtown, Kilbride, Lucan, Malahide., Merrion, Mount Jerome,
  Newcastle-Lyons, Old Kill, Rathfarnham, Rathmichael, Swords, Tallaght,
  Taney, & Whitechurch.
- County Dublin Cemetery Records, Ireland
  http://interment.net/ireland/dublin.htm
  Includes indexes to inscriptions from Balgriffin, Ballbriggan, Ballmadun,
  Bohernabreena, Castleknock, Clonsilla, Dardistown, Deans Grange,
  Donabate, Fingal, Finglass, Garristown, Glasnevin, Grallagh,
  Grangegorman, Grangegorman, Kilbarrack, Kilternan, Lusk, Malahide,
  Mulhuddart, Saint Margaret, Skerries, Sutton, Swords Village, Tallaght,
  The Ward, & Whitestown.
- Dublin Headstone Photos
  **www.igp-web.com/IGPArchives/ire/dublin/photos/tombstones/
  markers.htm**
  Pages from Carrickbrennan, Cruagh, Dalkey, Dublin, Dundrum,
  Glasnevin, Glencullen, Inchicore, Kilgobbin, Kilternan, Mount Jerome,
  Rathfarnham, Rathmichael, Saggart, Stillorgan, Sutton, Templeogue, &
  Whitechurch, etc.
- Thinking of Genealogy, Ireland, County Dublin
  www.the-e-site.com/irish/countydubli.htm
  Includes cemeteries at Ballmudan, Deans Grange, Garristown, &
  Grallagh.
- Graveyards and transcripts for Dublin, ordered by civil parish.
  **www.irishtimes.com/ancestor/fuses/counties/index.cfm?
  fuseaction=graveyards&CityCounty=Dublin**
  List.

- Monumental Brass Rubbings for Ireland: Dublin
  **www.ashmolean.org/ash/departments/antiquities/brass/counties/
  Dublin.html**
  In the Ashmolean Museum, Oxford
- Dublin Memorials of the Great War, 1914-1918
  http://homepage.eircom.net/~wlawless/ww1/Dublin.htm

Dublin

- The registers of S. Catherine, Dublin, 1636-1715
  http://search.ancestry.co.uk/search/db.aspx?dbid=28929
  Pay per view. From a printed book. Also available (pay per view) at
  **www.worldvitalrecords.com/indexinfo.aspx?ix=qcd_
  registersofscatherined_Dublin_**
- The registers of St. John the Evangelist, Dublin : 1619 to 1699
  http://search.ancestry.co.uk/search/db.aspx?dbid=28932
  Pay per view. From a printed book. Also available (pay per view) at
  **www.worldvitalrecords.com/indexinfo.aspx?ix=qcd_
  registersofstjohntheevangelist**
- Dublin, St. Marys, Marriages 1697-1800
  www.ajmorris.com/dig/toc/dubres.htm
  Scroll down to title. Subscription required. Index only.
- Register of St. Nicholas Without, Dublin. 1694-1739
  **www.worldvitalrecords.com/indexinfo.aspx?ix=ia_
  registerofstnich00dubl**
  Pay per view.
- Find your ancestors in The Parish Register Society Of Dublin, The
  Registers Of St. Patrick, Dublin, 1677-1800, 1907
  **www.findmypast.ie/articles/world-records/full-list-of-the-irish-
  family-history-records/life-events-birth-marriage-death/the-parish-
  register-society-of-dublin-the-registers-of-st-patrick-dublin-
  1677-1800-1907**
  Pay per view. From a printed book.
- The Register of the Parish of S. Peter and S. Kevin, Dublin
  http://search.ancestry.co.uk/search/db.aspx?dbid=28938
  Pay per view. From a printed book.
- The Register of the Parish of S. Peter and S. Kevin, Dublin, 1669 –
  1761
  **www.worldvitalrecords.com/indexinfo.aspx?ix=qcd_
  registeroftheparishofspeter**
  Pay per view. From a printed book.
- The registers of the Church of St. Michan, Dublin
  http://search.ancestry.co.uk/search/db.aspx?dbid=28955
  Pay per view. From a printed book.
- Find your ancestors in Registers Of The French Non-Conformist
  Churches Dublin 1701-1831
  **www.findmypast.ie/articles/world-records/full-list-of-the-irish-
  family-history-records/life-events-birth-marriage-death/registers-of-
  the-french-non-conformist-churches-dublin-1701-1831**
  Pay per view. From a book published by the Huguenot Society.
- Graveyards and transcripts for Dublin city, ordered by civil parish.
  **www.irishtimes.com/ancestor/fuses/counties/index.cfm?
  fuseaction=graveyards&CityCounty=Dublin**
  List.
- Inscriptions On the Monuments, Mural Tablets, &C at Present Existing in
  Christ Church Cathedral, Dublin
  **www.worldvitalrecords.com/indexinfo.aspx?ix=ia_
  inscriptionsonmo00finl**
  Pay per view. From a printed book.

Glasnevin

- Glasnevin Cemetery
  www.irish-genealogy-toolkit.com/Glasnevin-cemetery.html
  Introduction.
- Glasnevin Trust
  www.glasnevintrust.ie
  Includes database.
- Glasnevin Cemetery
  en.wikipedia.org/wiki/Glasnevin_Cemetery
  Encyclopedia article.

Howth

- Howth Co. Dublin Ireland: Transcript, Roman Catholic Cemetery, (St Mary's)
  http://freepages.genealogy.rootsweb.ancestry.com/~chrisu/ howth/howthcem.htm

Kinsealy *see* Baldoyle

Monkstown

- Extracts from the Parochial Returns of the Parish of Monkstown, Dublin
  www.ancestorsatrest.com/church_records/parochia_returns_ parish_monkstown.shtml
  Burials 1783-91.

Fermanagh *see also* Antrim

- Fermanagh Genealogy
  http://www.from-ireland.net/county-fermanagh-genealogy/
  Includes indexes to some civil registers, the graveyards of Aghalurcher, Aghavea, Donagh, St. Tierney's (Rosslea) and Tullynageeran (Tattynuckle); also list of Roman Catholic parish registers.
- County Fermanagh Northern Ireland Genweb
  www.rootsweb.ancestry.com/~nirfer/index.html
  Scroll down to 'Parish Names in Fermanagh', which includes pages for Aghalurcher baptisms, marriages & burials, 1814-15, & Inishmacsaint baptisms, marriages & burials, early 19th c. Also some marriage extracts from Aghavea, Belleek, Boho, Clones, Cleenish, Derryvullan, Devenish, Drumkeeran, Enniskillen, Galloon, Killesher, Kinawley, Magheracross, Magheraculmoney, Rossory, & Trory, etc.
- Ulster Ancestry Free Genealogy Pages
  www.ulsterancestry.com/ua-free-pages.php
  Includes Lisnaskea births, marriages, & deaths, 1804-1813 & 1813, inscriptions from Aghalurcher, Ballinamallard, Florencecourt, Galloon, Kinawley, & Tubrid, & Enniskillen's Boer War Memorial, 1899-1902, etc.
- Find your ancestors in Fermanagh Parish Registers: Baptisms
  www.findmypast.ie/articles/world-records/full-list-of-the-irish- family-history-records/life-events-birth-marriage-death/ fermanagh-parish-registers-baptisms
  Pay per view. For marriages see
  /fermanagh-parish-registers-marriages; for burials see **/fermanagh- parish-registers-burials**.

- County Fermanagh Roman Catholic Records
  www.rootsweb.ancestry.com/~fianna/county/fermanagh/ferrc.html
  Mostly held by the Latter Day Saints. There is a similar list at
  www.genuki.org.uk/big/irl/FER/RCRecords.html
- Find your ancestors in Fermanagh Cemetery Records
  www.findmypast.ie/articles/world-records/full-list-of-the-irish- family-history-records/life-events-birth-marriage-death/ fermanagh-cemetery-records
  Pay per view.
- County Fermanagh Gravestone Photo and Transcription Project
  www.tammymitchell.com/cofermanagh
- Graveyards and transcripts for Fermanagh, ordered by civil parish
  www.irishtimes.com/ancestor/fuses/counties/index.cfm? fuseaction=graveyards&CityCounty=Fermanagh
  List.
- Cemeteries Inscriptions
  www.igp-web.com/Fermanagh/Donated.htm#20
  Pages from Ardess, Bannagh, Caldragh, Carne, Carrick, Colaghty, Cross Breandrum, Derrygonnelly, Edenclaw, Enniskillen, Kiltierney, Kinawley, Lettercran, Magheraculmoney, Magherakeel, Montiaghroe, Muckross, Pettigo, Pubble, & Rossorry, in Excel format.
- Fermanagh GenWeb Page: Cemeteries of Fermanagh
  www.rootsweb.ancestry.com/~nirfer/cemeteries.html
  Includes inscriptions from Ardess, Drumully, Derrygonnelly, Irvinestown, Pettigo, & Tower.

Kinawley

- Kinawley Catholic Cemetery Co Fermanagh
  www.the-e-site.com/irish/FERMANAGH/Deaths/kinawley- catholic-cemetery-co-fermanagh.html

Slavin

- Slavin Church Burial Plots, County Fermanagh
  www.rootsweb.com/~nirfer2/Documents/Cemeteries/Slavin_ Graveyard_Plot_List.doc

Galway

- Galway Genealogy
  www.from-ireland.net/county-galway-genealogy
  Includes indexes to some civil registers, to Mullagh baptisms, 1859-67, & to Oranmore baptisms, 1833-6 & marriages 1833-7; also list of Roman Catholic parish registers on microfilm, etc.
- County Galway Genweb Project: Death Records
  www.rootsweb.ancestry.com/~irlgal/death_records.htm
  Several pages of extracts from the civil registers, late 19th c.
- County Galway Roman Catholic Records
  www.rootsweb.ancestry.com/~fianna/county/galway/galrc.html#
  Held by the Latter Day Saints.
- Baptism Records Galway
  www.rootsweb.ancestry.com/~irlgal/baptism_records.htm
  Various brief extracts from parish registers.
- Marriage Records, Galway
  www.rootsweb.ancestry.com/~irlgal/marriage_records.htm
  Various brief extracts from parish registers.
- Death Records, Galway
  www.rootsweb.ancestry.com/~irlgal/death_records.htm
  Various brief extracts from civil registers.
- Graveyards and transcripts for Galway, ordered by civil parish
  www.irishtimes.com/ancestor/fuses/counties/index.cfm? fuseaction=graveyards&CityCounty=Galway
  List.
- County Galway Cemetery Records, Ireland
  http://interment.net/ireland/galway.htm
  Includes indexes of inscriptions from Bohermore, Clarinbridge, Creagh, Kilcamin, Kilcummin, Oranmore, Portumna, Rahoon, Renvyle, Rinville, & Toorena.
- Thinking of Genealogy, Ireland: County Galway
  www.the-e-site.com/irish/countygalwa.htm
  Includes inscriptions from Kilcummin, Portumna, Renvyle,, & Tooorena, etc.

- Find your ancestors in Memorials Of The Dead: Galway & Mayo
  www.findmypast.ie/articles/world-records/full-list-of-the-irish-family-history-records/life-events-birth-marriage-death/memorials-of-the-dead-galway-and-mayo
  Pay per view.

Ahascragh

- Galway, Ahascragh, Church of Ireland Baptisms 1787-18[25]
  www.ajmorris.com/dig/toc/galres.htm
  Scroll down to title. Subscription required.

Beagh

- Beagh Parish, Galway: Baptisms 1860-61
  www.celticcousins.net/ireland/beaghbaptisms60to61.htm
  Continued for 1862 at **/beaghbaptisms1862.htm**
- Beagh Parish, Galway Baptisms,
  www.celticcousins.net/ireland/beaghbaptisms.htm
  Roman Catholic, covers 1850-51, 1855-7. For marriages, 1860-63, see **/beaghmarriages.htm**
- Inscriptions from Shanaglish, Beagh Parish, Galway
  www.celticcousins.net/ireland/cembeagh.htm

Glinsk

- Glinsk Parish Records 1836 – 1851
  www.rootsweb.ancestry.com/~irlgal/GLINSK2%20Births% 201836.1851.htm
  Baptisms. Continued for 1851-76 at **/1851_1876_glinsk_parish_baptisms.htm.**

Killaronan *see* Killian

Killeenadeem

- Killeenadeem and Kilteskill, May 1, 1836 through December 12, 1880
  www.rootsweb.ancestry.com/~irlgal/index30.htm
- Diocese of Clonfert, Parish of Killeenadeema: Baptisms, May 1, 1836 - December 12, 1880.
  Extractions from LDS Film #0979689 Co. Galway
  www.rootsweb.ancestry.com/~irlgal/index12.htm

Killian

- Diocese of Elphin, Parish of Killian and Killaronan Baptisms May 17, 1860 - November 21 1880
  www.rootsweb.ancestry.com/~irlgal/index26.htm
  Continued at **/index28.htm**

Kilteskill *see* Killeenadeem

Kiltulla

- County Galway, Diocese of Clonfert, Parish of Kiltulla: Townlands of Gloves, Lower Gloves, Elphin Gloves: Deaths, Baptisms, and Marriages: Extractions from LDS Film 1279216
  www.rootsweb.ancestry.com/~irlgal/index16.htm
  Extracts, c.1828-53
- Co. Galway, Diocese of Clonfert, Parish of Kiltulla (Townland of Gloves) Baptisms: , June 25, 1844 - January 15, 1854: Extractions from LDS Film #0979689
  www.rootsweb.ancestry.com/~irlgal/index15.htm

Roundstone

- Marriages: Parish Register Catholic Chapelry of Roundstone, Parish of Moyrus, Galway 1888-1889
  www.rootsweb.ancestry.com/~irlgal/index10.htm

Kerry

- Kerry Genealogy
  www.from-ireland.net/county-kerry-genealogy/
  Includes indexes to some civil registers, & to inscriptions from Bonane, Feaghna, Knockbrack Burial Ground and Lixnaw, etc.
- County Kerry: Superintendent Regisrar's Districts
  www.rootsweb.ancestry.com/~irlker/district.html
- Irish Genealogy.ie: Irish Church Records
  http://churchrecords.irishgenealogy.ie/churchrecords
  Includes index to many Co.Kerry Church of Ireland and Roman Catholic parish registers.
- Baptism/Birth Records
  www.rootsweb.ancestry.com/~irlker/birth.html
  For Co. Kerry, from various sources. For marriages, see **/marriage.html**. For burials, see **/death.html.**

- Registration Districts in County Kerry
  http://homepage.eircom.net/~dinglemaps/genuki/KER/Regdists.html
- County Kerry Baptism/Birth Records
  www.igp-web.com/Kerry/birthreg.html
  From a few miscellaneous sources.
- Marriage Records
  www.igp-web.com/Kerry/marreg.html
  Including civil registers from Annascall, Castlegregory & Dingle registration districts, 1864-1870
- County Kerry Death/Burial Records
  www.igp-web.com/Kerry/death.html
  Miscellaneous entries from Castlegregory Registration District, 1864-70.
- Family History Center Library Catalog Parish Register Film Numbers for County Kerry
  www.rootsweb.ancestry.com/~irlker/parfilm.html
- Kerry Local Authorities - Graveyard Records
  www.kerrylaburials.ie/en/Index.aspx
  Digitised images of registers.
- County Kerry Church of Ireland Records
  www.rootsweb.ancestry.com/~fianna/county/kerry/kercoi.html
- County Kerry Roman Catholic Records
  www.rootsweb.ancestry.com/~fianna/county/kerry/kerrc.html
- Baptisms/Birth Records,
  www.rootsweb.ancestry.com/~irlker/birth.html
  Contributed records for Co. Kerry
- Marriage Records, County Kerry, Ireland
  www.rootsweb.ancestry.com/~irlker/marriage.html
  Contributed records
- Burial/Death Records
  www.rootsweb.ancestry.com/~irlker/death.html
  Contributed records for Co. Kerry.
- Thinking of Genealogy, Ireland: County Kerry
  www.the-e-site.com/irish/countykerry.htm
  Includes civil marriages at Annascall, Castle Gregory, & Dingle, 1864-70; also cemeteries at Brosna & Castle Gregory.

- Graveyards and transcripts for Kerry, ordered by civil parish
  www.irishtimes.com/ancestor/fuses/counties/index.cfm?
  fuseaction=graveyards&CityCounty=Kerry
  List.
- Kerry Cemetery Records
  www.igp-web.com/IGPArchives/ire/kerry/cem.htm
  Miscellaneous pages, mostly brief.
- Kerry Headstone Photos
  www.igp-web.com/IGPArchives/ire/kerry/photos/tombstones/
  markers.htm
  From many cemeteries.
- Gravestone Inscriptions of Kerry Emigrants, St. Brigid's Cemetery, Hadley, MA
  www.rootsweb.ancestry.com/~irlker/hdleygrave.html
- Kerry's World War I Dead
  www.kerrylibrary.ie/   www1intro.asp

Annascall
- Birth Records: Civil Registration for the District of Annascall 1864, 1865, 1873 & 1975
  www.rootsweb.ancestry.com/~irlker/birthannasc6475.html
- Annascall Marriages: Civil Registration Annascall Registrar's District 1864-1870
  www.rootsweb.ancestry.com/~irlker/maranna1.html

Brosna
- Brosna Cemetery Inscriptions
  www.bluegumtrees.com/brosnakerry/Cemetery.html

Castlegregory
- Civil Registration of Marriages, Castlegregory Registrar's District, Dingle P.L.U. 1864-1870
  www.rootsweb.ancestry.com/~irlker/marcast1.html

Dingle
- Dingle Marriages: Civil Registration: Dingle Registrar's District 1864-1870
  www.rootsweb.ancestry.com/~irlker/mardingle1.html

- Civil Registration of Marriage: Castlegregory Registrars District: Dingle P.L.U, 1864-1870
  www.rootsweb.ancestry.com/~irlker/marcast1.html

Keel
- Catholic Parish of Keel and Kiltallagh, Co. Kerry: Marriage Records 1804 1820
  www.myirishancestry.com/about-us/articles/kerry/catholic-parish-of-keel-and-kiltallagh-co-kerry-marriage-records-1804-1820

Killarney
- Cemetery: Kerry, Killarney Church and Kilmankilloge Churchyard Memorials
  www.igp-web.com/IGPArchives/ire/kerry/cemeteries/
  killarney-kilmankilloge.txt

Killorglin
- Civil Registration Birth Records: Registrar's District of Killorglin
  www.rootsweb.ancestry.com/~irlker/birthkillorg.html
  For 1866, 1872 & 1875.
- Killorglin Tombstone Inscriptions
  www.rootsweb.ancestry.com/~irlker/tombkillor.html

Kilmankilloge *see* Killarney

Kiltallagh *See* Keel

Kinard
- Kinard - Burial Ground
  http://homepage.eircom.net/~dinglemaps/genuki/KER/Kinard/
  burials.htm

Listowel
- Birth Records: Civil Registration for the District of Listowel, 1875-1877
  www.rootsweb.ancestry.com/~irlker/birthlistow.html
- Cemetery Inscriptions: Listowel Area
  www.rootsweb.ancestry.com/~irlker/tomblist.html

Milltown
- Milltown Tombstone Inscriptions
  www.rootsweb.ancestry.com/~irlker/tombmilltown.html

Minard
- Minard - Aglish Burial Ground
  **http://homepage.eircom.net/~dinglemaps/genuki/KER/Minard/
  aglishburials.htm**

Tralee
- Baptism Records: Tralee
  www.rootsweb.ancestry.com/~irlker/birthtral.html
  Newspaper birth notices, 1771-97 & 1807-11.
- Tralee Parish Registers, Co. Kerry, Ireland
  **www.igp-web.com/IGPArchives/ire/kerry/church/tralee%
  20parish.txt**
  Includes 'various documentary records' of births marriages and deaths.
- Tralee War Memorial.
  **www.rootsweb.ancestry.com/~irlker/traleewarmem.html
  www.igp-web.com/Kerry/traleewarmem.html**

Trughanacmy
- An Extract of Kerry Marriages in the Barony of Trughanacmy
  www.geocities.ws/irishancestralpages/KMmain.html
  For 1874-84.

Valentia Island
- Headstone Inscriptions on Valentia Island: Kylemore Burial Grounds
  www.rootsweb.ancestry.com/~irlker/cemkylemore.html

Kildare
- Kildare Genealogy
  www.from-ireland.net/county-kildare-genealogy
  Includes indexes to some civil registers, & to inscriptions from Ardreigh,
  Athy, Celbridge New, Crosskeys, Fontstown, Harristown, Kilberry,
  Kildare Town, Killbegs, Knavinston, Monasterevin, Naas, Rathangan, &
  Toberara.
- County Kildare Roman Catholic Records
  www.rootsweb.ancestry.com/~fianna/county/kildare/kidrc.html
  Mostly held by the Latter Day Saints.

- Graveyards and transcripts for Kildare, ordered by civil parish
  **www.irishtimes.com/ancestor/fuses/counties/index.cfm?
  fuseaction=graveyards&CityCounty=Kildare**
  List.
- County Kildare Cemetery Records, Ireland
  http://interment.net/ireland/kildare.htm
  Includes indexes to inscriptions from Ballymore Eustace, Bodenstown,
  Celbridge, Clane Abbey, Eadestown, Kilcullen, & Kilshanroe

Ardkell
- Roundfort Parish, Co. Mayo, Tuam Diocese: LDS Film No. 1279209:
  Baptisms , 1899-1916 for the Townland Of Ardkell
  http://members.tripod.com/~Data_Mate/lists/ardkel.txt

Roundfort *See* Ardkell

Kilkenny
- Kilkenny Genealogy
  www.from-ireland.net/county-kilkenny-genealogy
  Includes indexes to some civil registers, Ballyraggett baptisms, 1850s,
  Castlecomer marriages, 1847-55, Clough baptisms, 1859-64, Freshford
  baptisms, 1773-75, 1777-80, 1800-01, 1805-06, & 1825, Johnstown
  baptisms, 1815-22 & marriages 1851-6, & Lisdowney marriages, 1828-
  32, inscriptions from Ballycallan, Ballyfoyle, Ballygurrim, Ballyhale,
  Bennetsbridge, Castlecomer, Castleinch, Clomantagh, Clontubrid,
  Coon, Cuffesgrange, Donaghmore, Dunmore, Freshford, Galmoy,
  Glenmore, Graine, Grangefertagh, Grove, Hugginstown, Jerpoint Abbey,
  Kilballykeeffe, Kilbride, Kilkenny, Kilmanagh, Knocktopher, Mill,
  Moneynamuck, Mullinarrigle, Paulstown, Rosconnell, Shanbogh,
  Slieveroe, Smithstown, Stoneyford, Thomastown, Thornback,
  Tulla,Tullaherin & Urlingford; also list of Roman Catholic parish registers
  on microfilm.
- County Kilkenny, Ireland, Parish Records
  www.rootsweb.ancestry.com/~irlkik/careclds.htm
  List with Latter Day Saints film numbers.

- County Kilkenny Ireland Genealogy: Parish Records at the National Libary of Ireland
  www.rootsweb.ancestry.com/~irlkik/parish_records_nli.htm
- County Kilkenny Catholic Parish Records
  www.rootsweb.ancestry.com/~irlkik/carecord.htm
- County Kilkenny Roman Catholic Records
  www.rootsweb.ancestry.com/~fianna/county/kilkenny/kikrc.html
  Mostly held by the Latter Day Saints
- Graveyards and transcripts for Kilkenny, ordered by civil parish
  www.irishtimes.com/ancestor/fuses/counties/index.cfm?
  fuseaction=graveyards&CityCounty=Kilkenny
  List.
- Kilkenny Cemetery Records, Ireland
  http://interment.net/ireland/kilkenny.htm
  Includes indexes of inscriptions from Bennettsbridge, Clara, Clontubrid, Kilkenny, Paulstown, Thomastown, & Tullaherin.
- Kilkenny Cemetery Records
  www.igp-web.com/IGPArchives/ire/kilkenny/cem.htm
  Includes pages from Black Friars Abbey, Blackrath, Callan, Castle Inchyloghan, Clough, Coolagh, Crettyard, Cross Hill, Kells, Kilbride, Kilkenny, Muckalee, Newtown Earley, Outrath, Sheestown, Thomastown, Tullaherin, Tullamaine, & Whitechurch, etc.
- Kilkenny Headstone Photos
  www.igp-web.com/IGPArchives/ire/kilkenny/photos/tombstones/
  markers.htm
  Miscellaneous photographs, including many from Listerlin.
- Gravestone Inscriptions
  www.kilkennyarchaeologicalsociety.ie/gravestoneinscriptions.htm
  List of holdings of Kilkenny Archaeological Society

Kilkenny
- Thinking of Genealogy, Ireland: County Kilkenny
  www.the-e-site.com/irish/countykilke.htm
  Includes some Kilkenny baptisms & marriages, 18-19th c.;
- St. John's (Maldin Street), Kilkenny: Baptisms, 1789-1841
  www.rootsweb.ancestry.com/~fianna/county/kilkenny/kik-mar3.html
- St. Mary's, Kilkenny: Baptisms 1772 to 1887
  www.rootsweb.ancestry.com/~fianna/county/kilkenny/kik-mar2.html

- St. Patrick's, Kilkenny Marriages 1800's
  www.rootsweb.ancestry.com/~fianna/county/kilkenny/kik-mar1.html

Kilmacow
- Kilmacow Parish Birth Index, County Kilkenny, Ireland (1858 to 1880)
  www.rootsweb.ancestry.com/~irlkik/records/kilmindx.htm

Thomastown
- Memorials of the Dead
  www.thomastownparish.ie/ourparish/memorials-of-the-dead
  Thomastown inscriptions.

Laois *See also* Carlow
- Laois Genealogy
  www.from-ireland.net/county-laois-genealogy
  Includes indexes to some civil registers, Arles baptisms, 1843-55, Ballyadams marriages, 1844-53, Clonaslee baptisms, 1859-78, & marriages, 1849-66, Durrow marriages, 1861-67, Graigue marriages, 1870s, Maryborough marriages, 1850-55, Mountmellick marriages, 1814-19, Rathdowney baptisms, 1790 & 1840-50, & marriages, 1840-50 & 1873-80; inscriptions from Abbeyleix, Acragar, Aghaboe, Aghnacross, Aharney, Anatrim, Arles, Attanagh, Aughmacart, Ballacolla, Ballinakill, Ballyadding, Ballyboodin, Ballybuggy, Ballyfin, Ballylynam, Ballyninan, Ballyroan, Bawn Hill, Bealady, Bordwell, Camross, Castfleming, Castletown Bridge, Chapel Cross Roads, Clonaslee, Clonenagh, Clonkeen, Clough, Coolkerry, Coolrain, Cross Roads (Raheen), Cullohill, Curraclone, Demesne, Donaghmore, Durrow, Dysart, Emo, Errill, Ironmills Bridge, Killabban, Killameestia, Killanure, Killenard, Killermogh, Kilmanman, Knockaroo, Kyle, Lea, Luggacurren, Mountmellick, Mountrath, Moyacomb, Ockanaroe, Pike of Rushall, Portarlington, Portlaoise, Portnahinch, Rahanavannagh, Raheen Raheensheera, Rathdaire, Rathdowney, Rathmiles, Rathsaran, Rosenallis, Roskelton, Rossmacowen, Sallyford, Shanahoe, Spink, Stradbally, Timahoe, Timogue, & Vicarstown; also list of Roman Catholic parish registers on microfilm.
- County Laois Roman Catholic Records
  www.rootsweb.ancestry.com/~fianna/county/laois/lexrc.html
  List, with LDS film numbers.

- Graveyards and transcripts for Laois, ordered by civil parish.
  **www.irishtimes.com/ancestor/fuses/counties/
  index.cfm?fuseaction=graveyards&CityCounty=Laois**
  List.

- Laois County Council: Graveyards
  **www.laois.ie/LeisureandCulture/Heritage/CulturalHeritage/
  Graveyards**
  Detailed survey.
- County Laois Cemetery Records, Ireland
  http://interment.net/ireland/laois.htm
  Includes indexes to inscriptions from the Rock of Dunamaise, &
  Stradbally,
- Laois Genealogy: Headstone Data
  www.genealogylaois.com
- Ancient Graveyards and Burial Places in Co. Laois
  www.rootsweb.ancestry.com/~irlcar2/Killeshin_index.htm
  List.
- Gravestone Inscriptions, Co. Laois
  **http://freepages.family.rootsweb.ancestry.com/~mjbrennan/
  inscriptions_index.htm**
  Includes inscriptions (with some photographs) from Arles, Ballylynan,
  Killabban & Killeen.

Aghaboe
- County Leix Baptism Records: Aghaboe RC Parish, pre 1796-Dec 1799
  www.connorsgenealogy.net/Leix/AghaboeBaptisms.htm
  Index.

Portarlington
- Find your ancestors in Thomas Philip Le Fanu, *Registers Of The French
  Church Of Portarlington, Ireland,* 1908
  **www.findmypast.ie/articles/world-records/full-list-of-the-irish-
  family-history-records/life-events-birth-marriage-death/thomas-
  philip-le-fanu-registers-of-the-french-church-of-
  portarlington-ireland-1694-1816**
  Pay per view. From a printed book published by the Huguenot Society.

Also available (pay per view) at
**www.worldvitalrecords.com/indexinfo.aspx?ix=ia_
registersoffrenc00port**

Leitrim
- Leitrim Genealogy
  www.from-ireland.net/county-leitrim-genealogy
  Includes indexes to some civil registers, & to Mohill baptisms, 1836-42;
  also list of Roman Catholic parish registers on microfilm.
- County Leitrim Roman Catholic Records
  http://www.rootsweb.ancestry.com/~fianna/county/leitrim/letrc.html
  List with Latter Day Saints' film numbers.
- Co. Leitrim
  http://homepage.eircom.net/~kevm/Co.%20Leitrim/co__leitrim.htm
  Includes indexes to headstones at Carrowcrin, Glenade & Glencar
- Graveyards and Transcripts for Leitrim, ordered by civil parish
  **www.irishtimes.com/ancestor/fuses/counties/index.cfm?
  fuseaction=graveyards&CityCounty=Leitrim**
  List.

Kinlough
- Kinlough Graveyard, Kinlough, County Leitrim, Ireland
  www.interment.net/data/ireland/leitrim/kinlough.htm

Limerick
- Limerick Genealogy
  www.from-ireland.net/county-limerick-genealogy
  Includes indexes to some civil registers, to Monegea baptisms, 1860-70,
  Newcastlewest baptisms, 1852-74, & St. Michaels' baptisms, 1820-23 &
  1845-54, & to inscriptions from Ardcanny, Limerick, Rathkeale; also
  includes list of Roman Catholic parish records.
- County Limerick Civil Parishes
  www.connorsgenealogy.com/LIM/Parishes.html
  List with notes on church registers.
- County Limerick Ireland: Civil Records
  www.connorsgenealogy.com/LIM/index.htm#civil records
  Includes a variety of extracts.

- Civil Parishes of County Limerick: Available Church Records
  www.genuki.org.uk/big/irl/LIM/Parishes.html
  List of parish registers.
- County Limerick Roman Catholic Records
  www.rootsweb.ancestry.com/~fianna/county/limerick/limrc.html
  Commencement dates only.
- Graveyards and transcripts for Limerick, ordered by civil parish
  www.irishtimes.com/ancestor/fuses/counties/index.cfm?
  fuseaction=graveyards&CityCounty=Limerick
  List.
- Limerick births, marriages and deaths, from the *Magazine of Magazines*
  1751-1761
  www.limerickcity.ie/Library/LocalStudies/BDMsfromthe
  MagazineofMagazines1751-1761/

Cappamore
- Cappamore, Tower Hill Cemetery
  www.countylimerickgenealogy.com/Cappamore/cappamore_
  tombstones.htm

Doon
- Doon Cemetery Headstones
  www.countylimerickgenealogy.com/Doon/index.htm

Kilbeheny
- Monumental Inscriptions from the Civil Parish of Kilbeheny
  http://freepages.genealogy.rootsweb.ancestry.com/~
  mccarthykathryn/kilbeheny_monumental_inscriptions.htm

Limerick
- Cemetery Records
  www.limerick.ie/historicalresources/archives/cemeteryrecords
  Database of 70,000 records from Mount St Lawrence Cemetery.
- Obituaries, death notices, etc. from the Limerick Chronicle
  www.limerickcity.ie/Library/LocalStudies/Obituariesdeath
  noticesetcfromTheLimerickChronicle/
  For 1780-1940; in annual files, partially indexed.

Oola
- Oola Graveyard Inscriptions
  www.countylimerickgenealogy.com/content/OolaGraveyard.html

Rathkeale
- Rathkeale Graveyard, Co, Limerick
  www.celticcousins.net/ireland/cemlim.htm

Londonderry *See also* Antrim (especially for the Bann Valley)
- Derry (Londonderry) Genealogy
  www.from-ireland.net/county-derry-genealogy
  Includes indexes to some civil registers, a list of Roman Catholic Parish registers on microfilm, & a list of 'Transcribed Gravestones References', i.e. published inscriptions, etc.
- Ulster Ancestry Free Genealogy Pages
  www.ulsterancestry.com/ua-free-pages.php
  Includes inscriptions from Glendermott, from St Columbs Cathedral, Londonderry, & from Londonderry war memorial.
- Genealogy Records Index
  www.rootsweb.ancestry.com/~nirldy2/Records/church/
  churchindex.htm
  Includes lists of Co.Londonderry Church of Ireland, Roman Catholic, and Presbyterian registers; also lists of cemeteries.
- Church Records of Derry: Church of Ireland
  www.igp-web.com/Derry/Records/church/derrycoi.html
- County Derry (Londonderry) Church of Ireland Parish Records
  www.rootsweb.ancestry.com/~fianna/county/derry/ldycoi.html
- Church Records of Derry: Presbyterian
  www.igp-web.com/Derry/Records/church/derrypres.html
- County Derry (Londonderry) Presbyterian Records
  www.rootsweb.ancestry.com/~fianna/county/derry/ldypres.html
- Church Records of Derry: Roman Catholic Churches
  www.igp-web.com/Derry/Records/church/derryrc.html
- County Derry (Londonderry) Roman Catholic Parish Records
  www.rootsweb.ancestry.com/~fianna/county/derry/ldyrc.html
- Derry Roman Catholic Parish Records
  http://vicki.thauvin.net/chance/ireland/derry/rcparish.jsp
  List, including LDS film numbers.

- Graveyards and transcripts for Derry, ordered by civil parish
  **www.irishtimes.com/ancestor/fuses/counties/index.cfm?
  fuseaction=graveyards&CityCounty=Derry**
- Cemetery Inscriptions
  www.igp-web.com/Derry/Records/church/derrycems.html
  List of transcripts for Londonderry.
- Cemetery Inscriptions
  www.rootsweb.ancestry.com/~nirldy/derrycems.html
  List of transcripts and locations.
- County Derry Cemetery Project
  http://www.igp-web.com/Derry/Cemeteries/cemindex.htm
  19 cemeteries; 'under construction'; at present only St. Patrick cemetery available.
- County Derry (Londonderry) Cemetery Inscriptions
  www.rootsweb.ancestry.com/~fianna/county/derry/ldytomb.html
  List of transcripts.
- Londonderry County Cemetery Records, Northern Ireland
  http://interment.net/uk/nire/derry.htm
  Includes index of inscriptions for St. Patrick's Cemetery, Sixtowns.
- Irish Genealogical Abstracts from the *Londonderry Journal*, 1772 – 1784
  **www.worldvitalrecords.com/indexinfo.aspx?ix=gpc0806350792_
  donaldmschlegel**
  Pay per view.

Bann Valley
- Northern Ireland: Bann Valley Family Information
  www.angelfire.com/falcon/bannvalley
  Includes Aghadowey (Londonderry) Church of Ireland marriages 1845-85, & inscriptions; Aghadowey Presbyterian marriages, 1845-63, & inscriptions; Bovedy (Londonderry) inscriptions; Desertoghill (Londonderry) inscriptions; Kilrea (Londonderry) inscriptions; Garvagh (Londonderry) Church of Ireland inscriptions; Garvagh Presbyterian baptisms, 1795-1849 & 1859-1934, marriages, 1795-1889, & list of tombstones; Moneydig (Londonderry) Presbyterian baptisms,, 1857-1923, & marriages, 1845-1928, & inscriptions; Moyletra Toy (Londonderry) inscriptions; The Vow (Antrim) inscriptions; etc.

- Bann Valley Genealogy: Church Records
  www.torrens.org.uk/Genealogy/BannValley/church/contents.html
  Note that this covers parishes in both Antrim & Londonderry. Includes Aghadowey (Londonderry) Presbyterian marriages, 1845-63 & inscriptions; Boveedy (Londonderry) Presbyterian baptisms, 1841-1928, marriages, 1842-1929, & inscriptions; Desertoghill (Londonery) inscriptions, Dunboe (Londonderry) inscriptions, Garvagh (Londonderry) marriages 1845-89, inscriptions & Presbyterian baptisms 1795-1824, marriages 1795-1802, 1807-14, 182289, & inscriptions; Kilrea (Londonderry) Presbyterian baptisms 1825-95; marriages 1825-45, inscriptions & candidates for communion, 1825-38; Maghera (Londonderry) inscriptions; Moyletra Toy (Londonderry) inscriptions, Moneydig (Londonderry) Presbyterian baptisms, 1857-1923, marriages 1845-1928, & inscriptions; Rasharkin (Antrim) inscriptions & Presbyterian marriages 1834-1919; Swatragh (Londonderry) Presbyterian inscriptions; Tamlaght (Londonderry) baptisms, 1842-66 & inscriptions; Tamlaght O'Crilly (Londonderry) inscriptions; Tobermore (Co.Londonderry) inscriptions; Vow inscriptions.

Clonmany
- Roman Catholic Marriages for the Parish of Clonmany (1852-1900)
  **www.iol.ie/~inishowen/genealogy/records/Clonmany/Marriage/
  index.html**
  Index

Glendermot See Tipperary. Dovea

Londonderry
- Find your ancestors in The Register Of Derry Cathedral 1642-1703
  **www.findmypast.ie/articles/world-records/full-list-of-the-irish-
  family-history-records/life-events-birth-marriage-death/
  register-of-derry-cathedral-1642-1703**
  Pay per view. From a printed book.

Moneydig
- Moneydig Presbyterian Church Records: Marriages
  **www.torrens.org.uk/Genealogy/BannValley/church/Moneydig/
  Marriages/1845-1889-mrgs.html**
  Covers 1845-1889.

Longford

- Longford Genealogy
  www.from-ireland.net/county-longford-genealogy
  Includes indexes to some civil registers, etc.
- County Longford Church of Ireland Church Registers
  www.igp-web.com/Longford/coi_parishes.htm
  List.
- County Longford Roman Catholic Records
  www.rootsweb.ancestry.com/~fianna/county/longford/logrc.html
- Church Records
  www.igp-web.com/Longford/churchrecs.htm
  Includes Ardagh & Moydow baptisms 1793-1895, marriages 1792-1895, and deaths 1822-95; Clonbroney baptisms 1828-99, marriages 1828-99 and deaths, 1828-92; Granard baptisms 1811-65, marriages 1778-1894, and deaths 1811-65; Kilcommock baptisms 1859-80, marriages 1859-80, and deaths 1859-80; Killoe marriages, baptisms, 1826-1917, 1826-1917, and deaths 1826-84.
- The Genealogy of County Longford: Church Records
  www.igp-web.com/Longford/churchrecs.htm
  Indexes to Ardagh & Moydow, Clonbroney, Granard, Kilcommock, & Killoe parish registers.
- County Longford Cemetery Records, Ireland
  http://interment.net/ireland/longford.htm
  Includes indexes to inscriptions from Ardagh & Drumlish.
- County Longford Headstone Photos
  http://www.igp-web.com/IGPArchives/ire/longford/photos/tombstones/markers.htm
  Includes photographs from Abbeyshrule, Ballinakill, Ballinamuck, Ballymacormack, Clondra, Cloontuskert, Corboy, Drumlish, Killoe, Newtownforbes, Old Cashel, Rathcline, & Shrule.

Newtownbond

- Newtownbond Church and Graveyard
  www.reocities.com/grymorgan

Newtownforbes

- Some Newtownforbes Baptisms
  www.igp-web.com/IGPArchives/ire/longford/churches/newtownforbes_bap.txt
  Covers 1829-41.

Louth

- Louth Genealogy
  www.from-ireland.net/county-louth-genealogy/
  Includes indexes to some civil registers, & to inscriptions from Ardee, Ballymakenny, and Termonfeckin.
- Church Records in Louth, Ireland
  www.rootsweb.ancestry.com/~irllou/Church
- County Louth Roman Catholic Records
  www.rootsweb.ancestry.com/~fianna/county/louth/lourc.html
- Graveyards and transcripts for Louth, ordered by civil parish
  www.irishtimes.com/ancestor/fuses/counties/index.cfm?fuseaction=graveyards&CityCounty=Louth
  List.
- County Louth Cemetery Records, Ireland
  http://interment.net/ireland/louth.htm
  Includes indexes to inscriptions from Calvary & Collon.
- County Louth Memorial Inscriptions
  www.jbhall.freeservers.com/memorial_inscriptions.htm
  List of published sources.
- Louth Cemeteries
  www.igp-web.com/IGPArchives/ire/louth/cem.htm
  Includes pages for Ballymascanlon & Dundalk, etc.
- Name Index to some County Louth Tombstone Inscriptions
  www.jbhall.freeservers.com/index_to_louth_inscriptions.htm
- County Louth Death Notices 1930-1940
  www.jbhall.freeservers.com/death_notices_1930-1940.htm
  From newspapers.

Carlingford

- Carlingford Heritage Centre Grave Markings & Genealogy Information
  http://carlingfordheritagecentre.com/index.php/genealogy
  Includes monumental inscriptions, etc.

Collon

- Collon-Dundalk Church Burials
  www.jbhall.freeservers.com/Collon%20-%20Louth%20Burials.htm
  Collon burials, 1791-1823; Dundalk, 1790-1802

Drogheda

- St Peter's, Drogheda registers 1702–1900
  http://ireland.anglican.org/about/185
- Louth Headstones: St. Peter's Parish Cemetery, Drogheda
  www.igp-web.com/IGPArchives/ire/louth/photos/tombstones/
  outh-drogheda-1/index.html
  Continued at **/louth-drogheda-2/index.html** & **/louth-drogheda-**
  3/index.html.

Dundalk *See* Collon

Haggardstown

- Haggardstown Roman Catholic Parish
  www.jbhall.freeservers.com/haggardstown_rc_parish.htm
  Burials from the *Dundalk democrat*, 1868-1900.

Kilsaran

- Louth, Kilsaran, Baptisms 1818-1840,
  http://www.ajmorris.com/dig/toc/loures.htm
  Index only. Scroll down to title. Subscription required.

Mayo *See also* Galway

- County Mayo Records
  www.irelandgenweb.com/irlmay/records.htm
  Includes Aghamore baptisms, 1864-1883 & marriages, 1864-82,
  Ballintober marriages 1839-1896, Bekan marriages, 1833-1910,
  Belmullet baptisms, 1861-1877, Ballysakeery baptisms, marriages &
  deaths, 1845-1896, Bohola baptisms & marriages, 1857-1901,
  Castlebar marriages, 1825 to 1831, Castlebar & Aglish marriages 1842-
  1879, Claremorris baptisms, 1835-82, & marriages 1806-1890,
  Kilconduff marriages, 1846-1878, Kilmoremoy baptisms, 1823-1830,
  1855, & 1866, Killala baptisms, 1854-1884, Kilmovee baptisms, 1854-
  1910, 1881-1913, & marriages, 1824-1848, 1854-1880, Knock baptisms
  1869-1905, & marriages, 1883-1943, Louisburgh baptisms 1850-1854,
  & Parke baptisms , & marriages, 1847-1911.

- Mayo Genealogy
  www.from-ireland.net/county-mayo-genealogy
  Includes indexes to some civil registers, to Bekan baptisms, 1832-71,
  Kilmovee marriages, 1824-27, & Templemore marriages, 1872-78; also
  list of Roman Catholic parish records.
- Mayo Ancestors
  www.mayoancestors.com/default.aspx
  Index to birth, marriage & death registers, c.1850-1900; also
  monumental inscriptions.
- County Mayo, Ireland: Church Records
  www.connorsgenealogy.net/Mayo
  Scroll down for Ballysakera baptisms, marriages & deaths (selected)
  1845-1896, Bohola baptisms & marriages 1857-1901, Lacken Roman
  Catholic baptisms 1853-55 & 1863-65, & marriages 1854-56, Turlough
  baptisms & marriages, 1847-1911, etc.
- County Mayo Roman Catholic Records
  www.rootsweb.ancestry.com/~fianna/county/mayo/mayrc.html
  Held by the Latter Day Saints.
- Births and Baptisms in Parishes Westport Castlebar, Co. Mayo & area
  freepages.genealogy.rootsweb.com/~deesegenes/birth.html
  Includes civil birth registrations, Co. Mayo, 1864, 1866-9, 1871-2, 1875,
  1877, 1880, 1905-7 &1912-13; baptismal registers for Aglish, 1822-
  1938, Aughagower 1828-1836, & 1842-80, Aughaval, 1845-1856,
  1862-1919, Backs 1854-63, Balla-Manulla 1837-71, Ballintober 1840-
  1881, Clare Island 1851-81, Crossmolina 1831-1838, Islaneady
  1839-1915, Lahardane 1865-79, & Newport 1879-1887, etc.
- Early Marriages in Westport, Newport, Aughagower, Kilgeever,
  Burriscarra, Mayo, Drum, Balla, Co. Mayo, Ireland
  http://freepages.genealogy.rootsweb.ancestry.com/~
  deesegenes/early.htm
  In the 1820s.
- Marriages in Parishes of Castlebar Westport Louisburgh, Ballintober-
  Achill, Co. Mayo area
  http://freepages.genealogy.rootsweb.ancestry.com/~deesegenes/
  marr.html
  Includes marriages in Aglish 1825-1932, Aughagower 1854 to 1879, Aughaval
  1823-1904, Balla, Roshlea & Drum 1837-65, Ballintober 1839-1881,
  Islaneady 1839-1916, Kilgeever, 1844-5, & Lahardane 1842 to 1862, etc.

- County Mayo Cemetery Records, Ireland
  http://interment.net/ireland/mayo.htm
  Includes indexes to inscriptions for Ballinasmallam, Ballindine, Ballinvilla, Bekan, Bohola, Claremorris, Cong, Kilcolman, Kilfian, Kilkinure, Lisloughry, Sleivemore, Swinford, & Tulrahan.
- Cemetery Index for County Mayo Ireland
  www.igp-web.com/Mayo/Cemeteries/index.htm
  Includes pages for Ballindine, Ballinvilla, Bekan, Crossboyne, Kilcolman, Kilfian, Sleievemore, & Tulrahan, etc.
- Headstones in North County Mayo
  www.goldenlangan.com/headstones.html
  22,000 photographs of headstones.
- Co Mayo
  http://homepage.eircom.net/~kevm/Co.%20Mayo/co__mayo.htm
  Index to headstones at Bushfield, Charlestown, Kilmovee, & Meelick.
- Extracts from Inscriptions in Westport Castlebar area
  http://freepages.genealogy.rootsweb.ancestry.com/~deesegenes/cem.html
  Includes extracts from Achill, Aughagower, Aughavale, Ballintubber, Ballovery, Ballyhean, Breagwy, Burriscarra, Burrishoole, Castlebar, Drum, Gloshpatrick, Islandeady, Kilbride, Kildownet, Kilgeever, Killawalla, Mayo Abbey, Murrisk Abbey, Neale, Old Castlebar, Rathbane, Slievemore, Straide, Tourmakeady, & Turlough.
- Cemeteries
  www.bernieworld.net/Cemeteries/The_Cemetery_Collection.htm
  Includes inscriptions from Aughavale, Burrishoole, Killeen, Kilmeena, Murrisk, & Slievemore; also list of burial grounds in Co. Mayo.

Ardkell See Roundfort

Bunlahinch
- Marriage Register of Bunlahinch Church - County Mayo for people who were converted from the Catholic Church to the Anglican Church, principally to obtain food to survive
  http://freepages.genealogy.rootsweb.ancestry.com/~deesegenes/bunlahinch.htm

Claremorris
- Claremorris Parish, County Mayo: Baptisms, 1835-1882,
  www.irelandgenweb.com/irlmay/records/ClaremorrisBaptisms.htm
- Claremorris Parish, County Mayo: Marriages, 1806-90
  www.irelandgenweb.com/irlmay/records/ClaremorrisMarriages.htm

Crossmolina
- Church of Ireland: Parish Church of Crossmolina
  www.celticcousins.net/ireland/mayocm.htm
  Baptisms 1768-1803.

Kilmoremoy
- [Baptisms, for Kilmoremoy Parish, 1823-1830, 1855, 1866]
  www.irelandgenweb.com/irlmay/records/KilmoremoyBaptisms.htm

Kiltimagh
- Kiltimagh, Co. Mayo church records: baptisms, July 1861 1 to September 1880
  www.rootsweb.ancestry.com/~fianna/county/mayo/kiltimaghb.html
- Kiltimagh, Co. Mayo, Roman Catholic Marriages
  www.rootsweb.ancestry.com/~fianna/county/mayo/maymar2.html

Midfield See Swinford

Rathfran See Steelaun

Roundfort
- Roundfort Parish, Co. Mayo, Tuam Diocese. LDS Film No. 1279209 Baptisms 1899-1916 for the Townland of Ardkell
  http://members.tripod.com/~Data_Mate/lists/ardkel.txt

Steelaun
- Steelaun and Rathfran Townland Baptismal Records, 1854 to 1884, Killala RC Parish
  www.irelandgenweb.com/irlmay/records/SteelaunRathfranBirths.htm

Swinford

- Midfield Cemetery also known as Brackloon Cemetery, Swinford, County Mayo, Ireland
  http://web.archive.org/web/20051031092256/http://www.
  celticcousins.net/ireland/midfieldcem.htm

Meath

- Meath Genealogy
  www.from-ireland.net/county-meath-genealogy
  Includes indexes to some civil registers, & to inscriptions from Athboy, Duleek, Dunboyne, Kells, Moy and Moyagher graveyards; also list of Roman Catholic parish registers on microfilm.
- County Meath Roman Catholic Records
  www.rootsweb.ancestry.com/~fianna/county/meath/mearc.html
  Mostly held by the Latter Day Saints.
- County Meath Cemetery Records, Ireland
  http://interment.net/ireland/meath.htm
  Includes indexes to inscriptions from Ardmulchan, Ashbourne, Athboy, Ballinlough, Ballymagarvey, Batterstown, Clonalvy, Crossmacole, Curraha, Donaghmore, Duleek, Dunderr, Dunsany, Dunshaughlin, Greenogue, Kentstown, Kilbride, Killegland, Kilmessan, Moynalty, Navan, Oldcastle, Rathfeigh, Ratoath, Retaine, Rooske, Skryne, Temple Kiernan, & Yellow Furze.
- Meath Cemetery Records
  www.igp-web.com/IGPArchives/ire/meath/cem.htm
  Includes pages for Athboy, Bathregan, Donore, Galtrim, Julianstown, & Monk Newton, etc.
- Meath Headstone Photos
  www.igp-web.com/IGPArchives/ire/meath/photos/tombstones/
  markers.htm
  Includes pages for Ashbourne, Athboy, Ballivor, Batterstown, Beauparc, Bective, Bohermien, Boyerstown, Brannockstown, Cannistown, Castlerickard, Castletown, Clonard, Dunboyne, Dunderry, Hill of Slane, Kentstown, Laracor, Navan, Nobber, Rathmolyon, & Trim, etc.
- Graveyards and transcripts for Meath, ordered by civil parish
  www.irishtimes.com/ancestor/fuses/counties/index.cfm?
  fuseaction=graveyards&CityCounty=Meath
  List.

Rathcore

- Rathcore Church Of Ireland, Co. Meath Church And Graveyard Inscriptions
  http://homepage.eircom.net/~Rathmolyongraveyard/directory/
  HOMER.html

Rathmolyon

- Rathmolyon Church Of Ireland, Co. Meath Church And Graveyard Inscriptions
  http://homepage.eircom.net/~Rathmolyongraveyard/directory/
  HOME.html

Monaghan

- Monaghan, Genealogy
  http://www.from-ireland.net/county-monaghan-genealogy/
  Includes indexes to some civil registers, & to inscriptions from Clones and Magheross; also list of Roman Catholic parish registers on microfilm.
- Ulster Ancestry Free Genealogy Pages
  www.ulsterancestry.com/ua-free-pages.php
  Includes Irish names in the marriage register of Portpatrick (Wigtownshire), 1720-1846, & inscriptions from Donagh.
- County Monaghan Church of Ireland Records
  www.rootsweb.ancestry.com/~fianna/county/monaghan/mogcoi.
  html
  List with locations. For other denominations, see:
  Presbyterian /mogpres.html
  Roman Catholics /mogrc.html
- Graveyards and transcripts for Monaghan, ordered by civil parish
  www.irishtimes.com/ancestor/fuses/counties/index.cfm?
  fuseaction=graveyards&CityCounty=Monaghan
- Monaghan Cemetery Records
  www.igp-web.com/IGPArchives/ire/monaghan/cem.htm
  Includes pages for Ballybay & Errigal Trough.

- Monaghan Headstone Photos
  www.igp-**web.com/IGPArchives/ire/monaghan/photos/tombstones/
  markers.htm**
  Includes pages from Aghabog, Annyalla, Ballyalbany, Bellinode, Ballybay,, Braddox, Cahans, Carrickatee, Carrickmacross, Clones, Clontibret, Coolshannagh, Donagh, Donaghmoyne, Drum, Drumkeen, Drumsnat, Ematris, Errigal Trough, Glennan, Inniskeen, Killeevan, Kilmore, Knocknacran, Latlurcan, Monaghan, Rockcorry, Smithborough, Stonebridge, & Tyholland, etc.

Kilmore

- Trinity Church (Stranoodan) Kilmore Parish, Co Monaghan, Ireland
  www.igp-web.com/IGPArchives/ire/monaghan/churches/trinity.txt
  Index to births & marriages, late 19th-early 20th c.

Offaly

- Offaly Genealogy
  www.from-ireland.net/county-offaly-genealogy
  Includes indexes to some civil registers, & to inscriptions from Ballymacmurragh, Bracknagh, Dunkerrin, Killeigh, Kilmachonna and Roscomroe; also includes list of Roman Catholic parish registers on microfilm.
- County Offaly Church of Ireland Records
  www.rootsweb.ancestry.com/~fianna/county/offaly/offcoi.html
  List; also includes Methodist & Quaker registers.
- County Offaly Roman Catholic Records
  www.rootsweb.ancestry.com/~fianna/county/offaly/offrc.html
- County Offaly Cemetery Records, Ireland
  http://interment.net/ireland/offaly.htm
  Includes index to inscriptions from Durrow.
- Offaly (Kings) Cemetery Records
  www.igp-web.com/IGPArchives/ire/offaly/cem.htm
  Includes pages for BallmacWilliam, Ballyburly, Banagher, Borrisnafarney, Clommacnoise, Croghan Hill, Old Croghan, Killeigh, Lynally, Raheen, & Urney, etc.
- Offaly Headstone Photos
  **www.igp-web.com/IGPArchives/ire/offaly/photos/tombstones/
  markers.htm**
  Includes pages for Durrow, Finglas, and Kilcommon, etc.

Finglas

- Registry of Internments Finglas, Co. Offaly
  **www.igp-web.com/IGPArchives/ire/offaly/cemeteries/finglas-
  graveyard.txt**
  Mid-20th c.

Killeigh

- Killeigh, Offaly, C.I. baptisms 1808–[1823]
  www.ajmorris.com/dig/toc/offres.htm
  Also marriages, 1809-31, & deaths 1808-34. Scroll down to title. Subscription required.

Rhode

- Offaly: Baptisms, 1866-1867, Parish of Rhode (RC)
  www.igp-web.com/IGPArchives/ire/offaly/churches/rhode-1866-67.txt
  Continued for 1868-75 at **/rhode-2.txt**

Roscommon

- Roscommon Genealogy
  www.from-ireland.net/county-roscommon-genealogy
  Includes indexes to civil registers, Athleague baptisms, 1808 & 1838-40, Boyle marriages, 1848-51, Geevagh marriages, 1851-55, & inscriptions from Kilglass; also list of parish registers on microfilm.
- Roscommon: Irish Parish Register
  www.rootsweb.com/~irlros/irish_parish_registers.htm
  List of registers for all denominations.
- County Roscommon Church of Ireland Records
  www.rootsweb.ancestry.com/~fianna/county/roscommon/roscoi.html
  List of registers.
- County Roscommon Roman Catholic Records
  www.rootsweb.ancestry.com/~fianna/county/roscommon/rosrc1.html
  List.
- County Roscommon Roman Catholic Records
  www.rootsweb.ancestry.com/~fianna/county/roscommon/rosrc.html
  Held by the Latter Day Saints.
- Graveyards and transcripts for Roscommon, ordered by civil parish
  **www.irishtimes.com/ancestor/fuses/counties/index.cfm?
  fuseaction=graveyards&CityCounty=Roscommon**

- County Roscommon Cemetery Records, Ireland
  http://interment.net/ireland/roscommon.htm
  Includes indexes to inscriptions from Assylinn, Elphin Town, Esternsnow, Kilcooley, Kilglass, Kilnamanagh, Kiltrustan, Shankill, Stokestown, & Tulsk.
- Roscommon Cemetery Records
  www.igp-web.com/IGPArchives/ire/roscommon/cem.htm
  Includes Castlerea, Dysart, Elphin, Esternsnow, Kilcooley, Kilglass, Kilnamanagh, Kiltrustan, Tisara, & Strokestown, etc.
- Roscommon Headstone Photos
  www.igp-web.com/IGPArchives/ire/roscommon/photos/
  tombstones/markers.htm
  Includes pages for Clooncraff, Croghan, Dysart, Killeenan, Killukin, Kilmore, Kilronan, Kilteevan, & Toomna, etc.

Baslic
- Baslic Cemetery
  http://homepage.eircom.net/~kevm/Co.%20Roscommon/Baslic/
  Baslic_2.htm

Drum
- Drum Cemetery
  www.drum.ie/cemetery
  Includes database.

Kiltullagh
- Find your ancestors in Kiltullagh Parish (RC) Baptisms,
  www.findmypast.ie/articles/world-records/full-list-of-the-irish-
  family-history-records/life-events-birth-marriage-death/
  kiltullagh-parish-rc-baptisms
  Covers 1839-81. For marriages, see **/kiltullagh-parish-rc-marriages.**
- Find your ancestors in Ireland Roscommon Kiltullagh Cemeteries
  www.findmypast.ie/articles/world-records/full-list-of-the-irish-
  family-history-records/life-events-birth-marriage-death/
  ireland-roscommon-kiltullagh-cemeteries
  Includes transcriptions of inscriptions from Ballinlough, Cloonfad, Granlahan, Kiltullagh, & Teamhair.

Roscommon
- Deaths from the Roscommon Town workhouse
  http://reocities.com/Heartland/Pines/7030/page2.html
  List, late 19th c.

Sligo
- Sligo Genealogy
  www.from-ireland.net/county-sligo-genealogy/
  Includes indexes to civil registers, & list of Roman Catholic parish registers on microfilm.
- County Sligo Church of Ireland and Methodist Records
  www.rootsweb.ancestry.com/~fianna/county/sligo/slicoi.html
  List.
- County Sligo Roman Catholic Parish Registers
  www.rootsweb.ancestry.com/~irlsli/parish1.html
  List.
- County Sligo Roman Catholic Records
  www.rootsweb.ancestry.com/~fianna/county/sligo/slirc.html
  List.
- Genealogy Records
  www.puregolduk.com/bren/kilglass_co_sligo3.htm
  Includes indexes etc to the parish registers of Castleconnor, Dromard, Easky, Kilglass & Skreen.
- Graveyards and transcripts for Sligo, ordered by civil parish
  www.irishtimes.com/ancestor/fuses/counties/index.cfm?
  fuseaction=graveyards&CityCounty=Sligo
  List.
- Burial in Sligo County Ireland
  www.rootsweb.ancestry.com/~irlsli/burialopen.html
  Covers many cemeteries, but only a few extracts from each.
- Sligo Cemetery Records
  www.igp-web.com/IGPArchives/ire/sligo/cem.htm
  Includes pages for Aghanagh, Ballymote, Ballysadare, Collooney, Gurteen, Kilvarnet, Sligo, Templeboy, & Templeronan , etc.

- Sligo Headstone Photos
  www.igp-web.com/IGPArchives/ire/sligo/photos/tombstones/markers.htm
  Includes inscriptions from Achonry, Aghanagh, Ahamlish, Ballinakill, Ballymote, Ballysumaghan, Calry, Collooney, Drumcliffe, Easkey, Geevagh, Grange, Gurteen, Kilvarnet, Riverstown, Roslea & Sligo.
- Burial in Sligo County Ireland
  www.rootsweb.ancestry.com/~irlsli/burialopen.html
  Monumental inscriptions for many cemeteries
- Co.Sligo
  http://homepage.eircom.net/~kevm/Co.%20Sligo/co__sligo.htm
  Index to headstones at Ahamlish, Ballinskill, Ballygawley, Banada Abbey, Calry, Carrigans, Curry, Drumcliffe, Keelogues, Kilmacowen, Killery, Scarden, Sooey, & Thurlestrane.
- County Sligo Cemetery Records, Ireland
  http://interment.net/ireland/sligo.htm
  Includes indexes to inscriptions from Ballisodare, Ballymote, Carrowanty, Collooney, Killaraght, Gurteen, Sooey, & Templeronan

Castleconnor
- Castleconnor Parish Records
  www.rootsweb.ancestry.com/~irlsli/castelconnoropen.html

Tipperary
- Tipperary Genealogy
  www.from-ireland.net/county-tipperary-genealogy
  Includes indexes to some civil registers, and to inscriptions from Ballingarry, Ballintemple, Corbally, Drom, Dungar, Grangemockler, Kilboy, Knock, Moyne, Templemore, Templeree, Templetuohy, Timoney and Uskane graveyards.
- County Tipperary Records: Church Registers
  www.irelandgenweb.com/irltip/records.htm#church
  Includes Borrisoleigh baptisms, 1815-1900, & marriages 1815-1900, Cahir baptisms 1845-1860, & marriages 1836-1845, Clerihan baptisms & marriages, 1852-1882 (indexes), Clonmel baptisms, 1840-1860, Clogheen baptisms1856, 1865-1868, 1870, Cullen & Latten baptisms 1846-1880, & marriages 1846-1889 (indexes), Glenbane baptism,1876-1897, Loughkeen/Birr baptisms, 1838-1847, & Templederry RC Parish

Baptism records, assorted names, 1842-1910. For cemeteries, see #graveyard. Includes inscriptions from Borrisoleigh, Emly, Glenkeen, Ileigh, Mount Bruis, Shronell, & Solohead.
- County Tipperary, Ireland
  www.connorsgenealogy.com/tipp
  Includes baptisms from Bansha, 1860-76, Cahir, 1845-60, Clogheen, 1856, 1865-8, 1870, Clonmel, 1840-1860, Emly, 1810-1820, & Loughkeen/Birr, 1838-1847; marriages Bansha, 1826-1860, Borrisoleigh, 1815-1900, & Cahir 1836-1845.
- Tipperary Family History Research
  www.tfhr.org
  Searches of Roman Catholic baptisms & marriages in the Archdiocese of Cashel & Emly.
- Cemetery Headstone Transcriptions Ireland
  http://members.webone.com.au/~sgrieves/cemetries__ireland.htm
  Collection of inscriptions from Ballinaclough, Barnane, Borrisoleigh, Dovea, Drom, Glenkeen, Ileigh, Inch, Kilfithmone, Kylanna, Loughmore, Powerstown, & Templemore; also Glendermott, Co. Londonderry, Leckpatrick, Co.Tyrone, Lurganboy, Co. Leitrim, & Manorhamilton, Co. Leitrim.
- County Tipperary Cemeteries
  www.irelandgenweb.com/irltip/TipperaryCemeteries.htm
  Fairly full list, including links to online pages.
- Tipperary Church of Ireland Registers
  www.igp-web.com/tipperary/coi_parishes.htm
- Parishes and Record Dates
  http://freepages.genealogy.rootsweb.ancestry.com/~irish/Tipperary/pardates.htm
  List of Church of Ireland and Roman Catholic registers for Tipperary.
- Quaker Records (surnames B, G & W) for County Tipperary
  www.igp-web.com/tipperary/quaker/index.htm
- Tipperary Parish Record Holdings
  http://www.igp-web.com/tipperary/holdings.htm
  Roman Catholic.
- County Tipperary Roman Catholic Records
  www.rootsweb.ancestry.com/~fianna/county/tipperary/tiprc.html
  Commencement dates only.

- Tipperary Births and Baptisms,
  www.igp-web.com/tipperary/births/index.htm
  Includes pages for Aghnameadle, Carrick on Suir, Clonmel, etc.
- Tipperary Marriage Records
  www.igp-web.com/tipperary/marriages/index.htm
  Includes pages for Aghnameadle, 19th c., Cashel 1654-7, Clonmel
  (RC), 1837-55, and the Registration Districts of Roscoe, Thurles &
  Tipperary, 1845-63, etc.
- Graveyards and transcripts for Tipperary, ordered by civil parish
  www.irishtimes.com/ancestor/fuses/counties/index.cfm?
  fuseaction=graveyards&CityCounty=Tipperary
- Cemeteries
  www.igp-web.com/tipperary/cemeteries/index.htm
  Includes pages for Bansha, Cahir, Castlegrace, Derrygrath, Inch,
  Kilaldriffe, Kilcommon, Loughloher, Marlfield, Mortlestown, Outrath,
  Rochestown, Shanrahan, Thurles, Templetenny, & Whitechurch.
- Tipperary Headstones
  www.igp-web.com/tipperary/tombstones/index.htm
  Database with photographs.
- Assorted Headstone Extracts
  www.igp-web.com/tipperary/cemeteries/misc_stones.htm
  From Tipperary.
- Cemetery Headstone Transcriptions Ireland
  http://members.webone.com.au/~sgrieves/cemetries__ireland.htm
  Mainly from Tipperary.
- County Tipperary Cemetery Records, Ireland
  http://interment.net/ireland/tipperary.htm
  Includes indexes to inscriptions from Ardcroney, Ballinree, Clonmel,
  Fethard, Grawn, Kilurane, Lisbunny, Lorrha , Modrneey, & Roscrea.
- Cemeteries in and around the Towns of Cahir, Clonmell, Cashel
  www.macatawa.org/~devries/Cemeteries.htm
  Includes monumental inscriptions from Ardfinnan, Ballylooby, Bansha,
  Cahir, Castlegrace , Derrygrath, Doughill, Kilcommon, Loughloher,
  Marlfield, Mortlestown, Outrath, Rochestown, Shanrahan , &
  Whitechurch.
- Assorted Tipperary Burials
  www.igp-web.com/tipperary/cemeteries/assorted_cems.htm

Ballylooby
- Ballylooby
  www.reocities.com/luanndevries/BALLYLOOBY.html
  Inscriptions.

Clonmel
- [Clonmel Births 1864 79]
  http://freepages.genealogy.rootsweb.ancestry.com/~irish/
  clonmel/clonbirt.htm

Dovea
- Irish Cemeteries: Dovea, Old Glendermott, Ileigh, Inch Old Cemetery
  http://members.iinet.net.au/~sgrieves/cemeteries_ireland_2.htm
  Inscriptions. Old Glendermott is in Co.Londonderry; O'Brien's Bridge in
  Co Clare.

Emly
- Emly Gravestone Inscriptions
  www.irelandgenweb.com/irltip/Records/EmlyGraveyard.htm
  List only.

Ileigh See Dovea

Inch See Dovea

Modreeny
- Tipperary, Modreeny, Baptisms 1835-18[40] ,
  www.ajmorris.com/dig/toc/tipres.htm
  Also marriages 1827-44.

Mt. Bruis
- Mt. Bruis Graveyard Inscriptions
  www.irelandgenweb.com/irltip/Records/EmlyGraveyard.htm

Shronell
- Shronell Graveyard Inscriptions
  www.irelandgenweb.com/irltip/Records/ShronellGraveyard.htm

Solohead

- Solohead Gravestone Inscriptions
  www.irelandgenweb.com/irltip/Records/SoloheadGraveyard.htm

Tyrone *See also* Antrim

- Tyrone Genealogy
  www.from-ireland.net/county-tyrone-genealogy
  Includes indexes to civil registers, to Pomeroy baptisms, 1869-72, & to inscriptions from Clonoe; also lists of Roman Catholic parish records.
- Church Records by Parish
  http://freepages.genealogy.rootsweb.ancestry.com/~
  　　　　　cotyroneireland/churchrecord/parishrecords.html
  List for all denominations.
- County Tyrone Roman Catholic Records
  www.rootsweb.ancestry.com/~fianna/county/tyrone/tyrrc.html
- Born Co. Tyrone, Buried Elsewhere
  www.cotyroneireland.com/menus/bburied.html
  World-wide in scope.
- County Tyrone: Birth Records
  www.cotyroneireland.com/menus/births.html
  Includes Aghaloo baptisms, 1802, Ardstraw birth announcements 1830-69, Aughnacloy birth announcements 1839-69, Aughnacloy Presbyterian baptisms & marriages, Ballygawley & Errigal Keerogue birth announcuments 1838-69, Bodoney birth announcements 1833-1869, Camus-Juxta-Mourne baptisms 1803-4, Camus births & christenings 1802-73, Cappagh birth announcements 1834-69, Clonfeacle birth announcements, 1839-69, Coagh civil births, birth announcements 1859-69, & Roman Catholic births, Clogher birth announcements 1836-68, Clogherny birth announcements 1843-68, Cookstown birth announcements 1838-69, Donacavey (including Fintona) birth announcements 1830-69, Donagheady birth announcements 1832-69, Donagheady Presbyterian baptisms 1838-1901, Donaghenry birth announcements 1838-68, Donaghmore birth announcements 1846-68, Drumragh baptisms, Drumragh birth announcements 1834-69, Dungannon birth announcements, Errigal Keerogue & Ballygawley birth announcuments 1838-69, Fintona birth announcements 1833-1868, Kilskerry birth announcements 1842-69, Leckpatrick birth announcements 1828-69, Longfield birth announcements 1841-68,

Lower Clonaneese Presbyterian baptisms 1840-1911, Strabane births 1828-69, Termonamongan birth announcements 1838-64, & Urney births 1836-69, etc.

- County Tyrone: Marriage Records
  www.cotyroneireland.com/menus/marriages.html
  Includes Aghaloo marriage announcements 1836-68 & Roman Catholic marriages 1837-1880; Ardstraw marriage announcements 1814-69; Aughnacloy marriage announcements 1833-1869; Bodoney marriage announcements 1787-1869; Bready Reformed Presbyterian marriages from 1847; Cappagh marriage announcements 1822-1868; Castlederg marriages 1846-1890; Coagh marriage announcements 1840-69; Clogher marriage announcements 1823-69; Clogherny marriage announcements 1838-69; Clonfeacle marriage announcements, 1832-69; Cookstown marriage announcements 1830-69; Donacavey Roman Catholic marriages 1866; Donacavey (including Fintona) marriage announcements 1830-69; Donagheady marriage announcements 1786-1869; Donagheady Presbyterian marriages 1838-1928; Donaghenry marriage announcements 1823-1869; Donaghmore marriage announcements 1830-1869; Donemana Presbyterian marriages 1845-1926; Dromore marriage announcements 1815-69; Dromore Roman Catholic marriages 1867-8; Drumragh marriage announcements 1785-1869; Dungannon marriages 1823-1850; Errigal Keerogue marriage announcements 1839-69; Fintona marriage announcements 1830-1869; Glenelly Presbyterian marriages 1845-50; Killyman marriage announcements 1830-68; Kilskerry marriage announcements 1831-68; Leckpatrick marriage announcements 1828-69, & marriages 1845-1932; Leckpatrick Presbyterian marriages 1845-1930; Longfield marriage announcements 1833-69; Magheramason Presbyterian marriages 1881-1927; Pomeroy marriage announcements 1836-69; Strabane marriage announcements; Termonamongan marriage announcements 1831-1869; Termonmaguirk marriage announcements 1830-1869; Tyrone marriages 1850-1860 & 1882; Urney marriage announcements 1822-1869, etc.

- County Tyrone: Burial & Death Records
  http://www.cotyroneireland.com/menus/burial.html
  Includes Aghyaran inscriptions, Ardstraw death announcements 1824-69, Aughnacloy Parish death announcements 1831-69, Australian death announcements re Co. Tyrone, 1859-1939, Ballygawley & Errigal Keerogue death announcements 1836-69, Bodoney Lower Parish Deaths 1815-69, Bodoney Upper deaths 1827-69, Cappagh death announcements 1829-69, St. Johns Church of Ireland, Castlederg burials 1839-1861, Castlederg New Cemetery 1931-1959, Clogher death announcements, 1826-68, Clogherny death announcements 1823-69, Clonfeacle death announcements 1830-69, Coagh death announcements 1838-69, Cookstown death announcements, 1824-69, Donacavey (including Fintona) death announcements 1787-1869, Donagheady deaths 1786-1869, Donaghenry death announcements 1830-69, Donaghmore death announcements 1832-69, Dromore death announcements 1822-69, Drumragh (including Omagh) death announcements 1822-69, Dungannon deaths 1828-50, Edymore & Cavanalee townlands & Camus, miscellaneous personal announcements 1823-1848, Gorestown inscriptions, Killyman burials, & death announcements 1822-67, Kilskeery death announcements 1835-68, Leckpatrick death announcements 1786-1869, Longfield East & Longfield West death announcements 1833-68, Lower Clonaneese Presbyterian deaths 1865-1912, Magherakeel inscriptions, Pomeroy death announcements 1859-69, Clonfeacle Inscriptions, Scarvagherin inscriptions, Sixmilecross, miscellaneous births, deaths, & marriages 1837-1946, Strabane death announcements, 1785-1869, Termonamongan death announcements 1832-69, Termonmaguirk death announcements 1835-67, Tyrone deaths 1811-1855 & 1861-1870 as reported in New York City newspapers, Urney deaths 1815-69, & miscellaneous burials 1837-60.

- County Tyrone: Church Records
  www.cotyroneireland.com/menus/churchrecord.html
  Includes Aghaloo baptisms 1846-1901, & marriages 1837-1880; Arboe baptisms; Aughnacloy baptisms 1823-1837, & marriages 1810-1839, Caledon baptisms 1791-1805; Cappagh baptisms - 1820, 1825, 1826, 1839; Castlederg marriages 1850-1890, & burials 1839-1861; Coagh baptisms; Derryloran baptisms 1797-1809, births, marriages, & deaths 1810-1896; Donagheady Presbyterian baptisms 1838-1901 & marriages, 1838-1926; Donemana Presbyterian baptisms 1861-1889; Dromore Roman Catholic baptisms; Drumragh baptisms; Glenhoy Presbyterian inscriptions; Killyman baptisms, marriages & burials; Leckpatrick Presbyterian marriages 1845-1930; Lower Clonaneese Presbyterian baptisms 1840-1911 & deaths 1865-1912; Magheramason Presbyterian marriages 1881-1927; Strabane Presbyterian baptisms 1828 to 1937, etc.

- Graveyards and transcripts for Tyrone, ordered by civil parish
  **www.irishtimes.com/ancestor/fuses/counties/index.cfm?
  fuseaction=graveyards&CityCounty=Tyrone**
  List.

- County Tyrone Cemetery Index
  www.rootsweb.ancestry.com/~irluie2/Cemetery/cemetery.html
  Photographs of gravestones from Aghaloo, Dunmoyle, Errigle Cross, Killeeshil, & Killens.

- County Tyrone: Graveyard Records and Photos
  www.cotyroneireland.com/menus/grave.html
  Includes pages for Ardstraw, Castlederg, Cookstown, Donaghcavey, onaghendry, Dromore, Mountcastle, Strabane, & Urney.

- Gravestones
  www.bangor.homecall.co.uk/index.htm
  Includes memorials from Killyman & Killycolpy.

- Tyrone Cemetery Records
  www.igp-web.com/IGPArchives/ire/tyrone/cem.htm
  Includes pages from Ardtrea, Benburb, & Donaghmore, etc.

- Tyrone Headstone Photos
  **www.igp-web.com/IGPArchives/ire/tyrone/photos/tombstones/
  markers.htm**
  Includes pages from Aughnagar, Beragh, Caledon, Carland, Castlecaulfield, Clonaneese, Crossdernott, Desertcreat, Donaghmore, Dungannon, Dunmoyle, Errigle, Fintona, Glenmornan, Killens, Kilskeery, Newtownstewart, & Strabane.

- Tyrone Constitution Deaths, 1882-1889
  **www.ancestryireland.com/family-records/tyrone-constitution-
  deaths-1882-1889**
  Subscription required. Newspaper announcements.

Bready

- Bready Ancestry: Genealogy
  www.breadyancestry.com/index.php?id=genealogy
  Includes Donagheady Church of Ireland baptisms & burials 1697-1800, & marriages, 1826-1922; Leckpatrick Church of Ireland marriages from 1845, Magheramason Presbyterian Church marriages, 1881-1927; also monumental inscriptions from Grange, Donagheady, & Old Leckpatrick; also Donagheady confirmations 1790-1900, & Vestry Book 1698-1723 -

Kilskerry

- Tyrone Church Records
  www.igp-web.com/IGPArchives/ire/tyrone/church.htm
  Primarily Kilskerry baptisms & marriages, 1767-1872, & deaths, 1796-1897.

Tyrone

- Find your ancestors in Tyrone Cemetery Records
  www.findmypast.ie/articles/world-records/full-list-of-the-irish-family-history-records/life-events-birth-marriage-death/tyrone-cemetery-records
  Pay per view. Inscriptions from St. John's Cemetery, Tyrone.

Waterford

- Waterford Genealogy
  www.from-ireland.net/county-waterford-genealogy
  Includes some indexes to civil registers, and to inscriptions from Kilmacow, etc.
- Waterford County Library: Death Register Database search
  http://locdat.waterfordcountylibrary.ie/ipac20/ipac.jsp?profile=death
  For the war dead, 1914-18, see **=war**. For grave memorials, see **=grave**.
- Waterford Church of Ireland Registers
  www.igp-web.com/Waterford/cofi.htm
  List.
- County Waterford Roman Catholic Records
  www.rootsweb.ancestry.com/~fianna/county/waterford/watrc.html
  Commencement dates only.
- Waterford Church Records
  www.igp-web.com/IGPArchives/ire/waterford/church.htm
  Includes page for selected Quaker births, marriages & deaths, etc.

- Graveyards and transcripts for Waterford, ordered by civil parish
  www.irishtimes.com/ancestor/fuses/counties/index.cfm?fuseaction=graveyards&CityCounty=Waterford
- County Waterford Cemeteries
  www.irelandgenweb.com/irlwat/watercem.htm
  Includes inscriptions from Lismore Famine Graveyard, Kilmacow, & Kilronan.
- Waterford Cemetery Records
  www.igp-web.com/IGPArchives/ire/waterford/cem.htm
  Includes inscriptions from Drumcannon, Dungarvan (St Mary's), Dunhill, Kilbarrymeaden, Kinsalebeg, Lismore, Stradbally, Tallow, Tramore, & Whitechurch.
- Waterford City and County Headstones
  www.igp-web.com/Waterford/headstones/index.htm
  Database of photographs.
- Waterford Headstone Photos
  www.igp-web.com/IGPArchives/ire/waterford/photos/tombstones/markers.htm
  Includes pages for Cheekpoint, Killea, Kilrossanty & Portlaw.
- Thompson's Funeral Books
  www.waterfordcouncil.ie/en/Resident/Library,Services/Burial,Records/Thompsons,Funeral,Books
  Database: undertaker's record of funerals, 1874-1918

Killea

- Co Waterford
  http://homepage.eircom.net/~kevm/Co.%20Waterford/co__waterford.htm
  Includes index to headstones at Killea.

Lismore

- Waterford, Lismore Cathedral Marriages 1692-[1867]
  www.ajmorris.com/dig/toc/watres.htm
  Scroll down to title. Subscription required.

Waterford

- Baptisms, and Marriages of Newfoundlanders performed at St. Patrick's Church, Waterford, Ireland, period of 1752-1770
  http://ngb.chebucto.org/Parish/bap-mar-waterford-1752-1770.shtml

Westmeath

- WestmeathGenealog
  www.from-ireland.net/county-westmeath-genealogy/
  Includes indexes to some civil registers, & to inscriptions from Delvin.
- County Westmeath Roman Catholic Records
  www.rootsweb.ancestry.com/~fianna/county/westmeath/
  wemrc.html
  List.

- Graveyards and transcripts for Westmeath, ordered by civil parish
  www.irishtimes.com/ancestor/fuses/counties/index.cfm?
  fuseaction=graveyards&CityCounty=Westmeath
- County Westmeath Cemetery Records, Ireland
  http://interment.net/ireland/westmeath.htm
  Includes indexes to inscriptions from Castlepollard, Castleton, Cornamagh, Fore, Killafree, Lickbla, & Turin.
- Westmeath Cemetery Records
  www.igp-web.com/IGPArchives/ire/westmeath/cem.htm
  Includes pages for Athlone, Castlepollard, Castletown, Drumcree, Drumlummon, Finea, Fore, Lickblay, Mullingar, & Raharney.
- Westmeath Headstone Photos
  www.igp-web.com/IGPArchives/ire/westmeath/photos/tombstones/
  markers.htm
  Includes pages for Finea, Multifarnham, & Russagh, etc.

Ardnurcher

- Memorials, Ardnurcher Churchyard, Co., Westmeath
  www.igp-web.com/westmeath/ardnurcher_memorials.html

Castlelost

- Memorials, Castlelost Churchyard, Co., Westmeath
  www.igp-web.com/westmeath/castlelost_mem.html

Killucan

- Parish of Killucan (Diocese of Meath): Combined Register & Vestry Minutes, 1696-1786
  http://ireland.anglican.org/cmsfiles/pdf/AboutUs/library/registers/
  Killucan_1696-1786.pdf

Mullingar

- Westmeath County Ireland Archives Church Records ... Baptisms , (Col) Mullingar 1877-1900
  www.igp-web.com/IGPArchives/ire/westmeath/churches/
  mullingar-bap.txt
  Index. For marriages, 1844-99, see **/mullingar-mar.txt**

Wexford

- Wexford Genealogy
  www.from-ireland.net/county-wexford-genealogy
  Includes some indexes to civil registers, New Ross baptisms, 1828-34 & 1841-71, & to inscriptions from Ambrosetown, Ardamine, Ballycanew, Ballyfad, Ballymagarret, Ballymitty, Bannow, Barntown, Bunclody, Camolin, Donoughmore, Ferns, Kilcavan, Kilgorman, Killenagh, Kilmanna (Cleriestown), Kilmyshal, Kilmyshal Old, Kilnahue, Kilrush, Kiltennel, Knockbrandon, Leskinfere, Monaseed, Prospect, Taghmon, & Templeshanbo; also list of Roman Catholic parish registers on microfilm.
- Wexford Church Records
  www.igp-web.com/IGPArchives/ire/wexford/church.htm
  Includes pages for Quaker births, marriages and deaths, Killinick, Rathanga, etc.
- County Wexford Roman Catholic Records
  www.rootsweb.ancestry.com/~fianna/county/wexford/wexrc.html
- Graveyards and transcripts for Wexford, ordered by civil parish
  www.irishtimes.com/ancestor/fuses/counties/index.cfm?
  fuseaction=graveyards&CityCounty=Wexford
- County Wexford Cemetery Records, Ireland
  http://interment.net/ireland/wexford.htm
  Includes indexes to inscriptions from Bunclody, Crosstown, Gorey, Hook, Kilmore, & Templetown.
- Wexford Cemetery Records
  www.igp-web.com/IGPArchives/ire/wexford/cem.htm
  Includes inscriptions from Ardcandrisk, Arklow, Ballyconnor Castle, Bannow, Clone, Duncannon, Duncormick, Gorey, Kildavin, Lady's Island, Old Ross, Piercestown, New Ross, & Toome.

- Wexford Headstone Photos
  www.igp-web.com/IGPArchives/ire/wexford/photos/tombstones/
  markers.htm
  Includes pages for Gorey, Hollyfort, Horetown, Inch, Monaseed, & Tagoat.
- New York Reference in County Wexford Gravestone Inscriptions
  http://freepages.genealogy.rootsweb.ancestry.com/~nyirish/
  Memorial%20Inscriptions%20NEW%20YORK%20references.html

Kilgarvan
- Kilgarvan Graveyard Headstones
  http://goldenlangan.com/graves-kv.html

Wicklow
- Wicklow Genealogy
  www.from-ireland.net/county-wicklow-genealogy/
  Includes indexes to some civil registers, & to inscriptions from Bray, Delgany, Derrylossary, Kilfea, Killenagh, Killoughter, Kilmacanogue, Kilmacanogue, Kilquabde, Moyacomb, Powerscourt, Roundwood, Tornant, & Valleymount; also includes list of Roman Catholic parish registers on microfilm.
- Wicklow Church Records
  www.igp-web.com/IGPArchives/ire/wicklow/church.htm
  Includes Arklow baptisms, & marriages, 19-20th c., Redcross burials 1881-8, Wicklow Methodist Circuit baptisms, 1820-1841 & many other assorted records.
- County Wicklow Church of Ireland Records
  www.rootsweb.ancestry.com/~fianna/county/wicklow/wiccoi.html
  For other denominations, see:
  Methodists, Presbyterians, & Quakers **/wicprot.html**
  Roman Catholics **/wicrc.html**
- Graveyards and transcripts for Wicklow, ordered by civil parish
  www.irishtimes.com/ancestor/fuses/counties/index.cfm?
  fuseaction=graveyards&CityCounty=Wicklow
  List.

- County Wicklow Cemetery Records, Ireland
  http://interment.net/ireland/wicklow.htm
  Includes indexes to inscriptions from Baltinglass, Davistown, Dunlavin, Glendalough, Heighington, Kilavaney, Kilranalagh, Leitrim, Manor Kilbride, Powerscourt, Rathbran, Tournant, & Tyneclash.
- Wicklow Cemetery Records
  www.igp-web.com/IGPArchives/ire/wicklow/cem.htm
  Includes pages for Arklow, Ballinure, Baltinglass Abbey, Delgany, Dunganstown, Hollywood, Kilcool, Kilranelagh, Kiltegan, Powerscourt, & Wicklow, etc.
- Wicklow Headstone Photos
  www.igp-web.com/IGPArchives/ire/wicklow/photos/tombstones/
  markers.htm
  Includes pages for Arklow, Askanagap, Avoca, Ballinatone, Baltyboys, Blessington, Bray, Calary, Conary, Curtlestown, Delgany, Derralossary, Ennereilly, Ennisboyne, Enniskerry, Glendalough, Greystones, Hollywood, Kilbride, Kilcarra, Kilcommon, Kilcoole, Killadreenan, Killiskey, Killmurray, Killoughter, Kilmacanogue, Kilmagig, Kilquade, Kiltegan, Little Bray, Newcastle, Rathbran, Rathnew, Redford, Roundwood, Templeboden, & Wicklow, etc.
- Search County Wicklow Graveyards for your Ancestors
  www.rootsweb.ancestry.com/~irlwic2/grave_yards/
  Includes inscriptions from Arklow, Avoca, Ballimatone, Barranisky, Conary, Ennisboyne, Glendalough, Greenane, Kilbride, Powerscourt, & Wicklow.

Arklow
- Arklow Church Records
  www.igp-web.com/IGPArchives/ire/wicklow/arklow.htm
  Indexes to baptisms & marriages, 19-20th c.

Dunganstown
- Dunganstown Parish Records, Wicklow, Ireland, Baptisms , 1842-1910
  www.ancestorsatrest.com/church_records/dunganstown_
  parish_register_wicklow.shtml
  Surnames only.

Kilmurry
- Find your ancestors in Wicklow Cemetery Records
  **www.findmypast.ie/articles/world-records/full-list-of-the-irish
  -family-history-records/life-events-birth-marriage-death/
  wicklow-cemetery-records**
  Pay per view. Inscriptions from Old Kilmurry Roman Catholic Cemetery.

9. Other Sources

Information on a wide range of sources is available on the net. This includes much valuable advice; it also includes many sites providing the actual data. A wide variety of sources have sites devoted to them; these are listed here, prefaced by a listing of sites with database and source collections.

- DIGdat: Digital Irish Genealogy Data
  www.ajmorris.com/dig
  Pay per view, but some free data; also many fiche offered for sale.
- Irish Chronicles Project
  www.ajmorris.com/dig/toc/_010icp.htm
  Numerous brief extracts from sources, primarily from a newsletter published between 1996 & 2003. Pay per view.
- Fáilte Romhat
  www.failteromhat.com
- Find My Past
  www.findmypast.ie
  One of the major commercial hosts.
- Irish Family Research
  www.irishfamilyresearch.co.uk
  Collection of databases, including many local ones not otherwise listed here. Subscription required.
- Irish Origins
  www.irishorigins.com
  Pay per view. The databases on this site have just been transferred to **www.findmypast.com**
- Irish Record Collection 1536-1932
  www.familyrelatives.com/articles/details.php?aid=48
  Mainly pay per view; c.20 databases of minor sources.

- Roots Ireland
  www.rootsireland.ie
  Databases of the Irish Family History Foundation, including birth, marriage & death records, census, gravestone inscriptions, Griffith's Valuation, passenger lists, & various census substitutes, not otherwise listed below. Over 20,000,000 records.
- Thinking of Genealogy: Ireland
  www.the-e-site.com/irish/index.htm
  Pages for every county.
- Ulster Historical Foundation: Irish Genealogy Databases
  www.ancestryireland.com/search-irish-genealogy-databases/
  Extensive collection of databases; subscription required for most.
- Irish Source Records 1500s-1800s
  www.genealogy.com/275facd.html
  Subscription based index to census, land, marriage, and probate records.
- A Little Bit of Ireland
  www.celticcousins.net/ireland/index.htm
  Mainly transcriptions of original sources.
- Ancestry
  www.ancestry.co.uk
  Pay per view. The largest international collection of commercial databases. Click 'search', 'card catalogue', & 'Ireland' for a list of over 140 Irish databases (many of which are listed here).
- World Vital Records: Ireland
  www.worldvitalrecords.com/contentsearch.aspx?p=Ireland
  Over 300 databases.
- Irish Manuscripts Commission
  www.irishmanuscripts.ie
  Publishers of many sources for Irish history, some of which have been digitised & are separately listed here.
- Casey's Remarkable Collection of Genealogical Sources for Kerry and Cork ... and How to Use It
  www.rootsweb.ancestry.com/~irlker/pdf/caseyaid.pdf
  Detailed description of a genealogist's collection of notes on 3,000,000 names

- Irish Records Index 1500-1920
  http://search.ancestry.co.uk/search/db.aspx?dbid=4077
  Pay per view. Index to a miscellaneous collection gathered after the destruction of the Irish Public Record Office in 1922.
- Irish Records Extraction Database
  http://search.ancestry.co.uk/search/db.aspx?dbid=3876
  c.100,000 records from 120 different sources - but little indication of where the information came from.
- Clare County Library: Online Records
  www.clarelibrary.ie/eolas/coclare/genealogy/genealog.htm
  See also **www.clarelibrary.ie/eolas/library/local-studies/clasp/ online_publications/online_publications.htm**
  Collection of databases for Clare.

Admiralty Examinations
- High Court of Admiralty Examinations, 1536-1641: material relating to Ireland
  www.from-ireland.net/history/admirindex/admirintrolinks.htm
  Surname index.

Agricultural Census
Antrim
- 1803 Agricultural Census of Antrim
  www.ancestryireland.com/family-records/agricultural-census-of- antrim-1803/Membership required
  Subscription required.

Down
- Agricultural Census of Down, 1803
  www.ancestryireland.com/family-records/1803-agricultural- census-county-down
  Subscription required.
  See also **/agricultural-census-of-some-parishes-in-county-down-1803**

Aliens' Registers
- The Aliens Register 1914-1918: Dublin Metropolitan Police (DMP) A Division, Dublin
  www.familyhistory.ie/docs/aliens/Aliens.pdf

Assizes

Antrim

- County Antrim Assizes Court in Carrickfergus in 1839
  www.rootsweb.ancestry.com/~fianna/NIR/antrim1839.htm
  Lists prisoners tried.

Louth

- County Louth Assizes, 1775-1810
  www.jbhall.freeservers.com/louth_assizes_1793-99.htm

Tyrone

- County Tyrone: Criminals
  www.cotyroneireland.com/menus/criminals.html
  Includes manay extracts from Assize records, 1815-37, etc.

Westmeath

- Westmeath Ireland Genealogy: Return of all Offences committed in the
  above County since Summer Assizes 1869 to Spring Assizes 1870
  www.igp-web.com/westmeath/assize.html
  Continued from Summer Assizes 1870 at **/assize2.html**

Business Records

- Your Family Tree, 18: Business Records
  www.proni.gov.uk/no.18_-_business_records__73kb_.pdf
  In the Public Record Office of Northern Ireland.
- The Harland & Wolff Papers
  www.proni.gov.uk/introduction__harland_and_wolff_d2805.pdf
  Description of business records of the ship builders; including staff
  records.

Catholic Qualification Rolls

- Research Help: Convert Rolls Explanation and Examples
  **www.from-ireland.net/research-help-convert-rolls-explanation-
  examples**

Donegal

- State Papers: Catholic Qualification Rolls, 1778-1790. Donegal
  www.ulsterancestry.com/ShowFreePage.php?id=238
  See also **=274.**

Fermanagh

- Catholic Qualifation Rolls, Co. Fermanagh
  www.from-ireland.net/catholic-qualification-rolls-fermanagh

Galway

- The Catholic Convert Rolls Explanation, Co. Galway
  www.from-ireland.net/catholic-convert-rolls-galway

Monaghan

- Catholic Qualification Rolls: County Monaghan c.1778
  **www.ulsterancestry.com/
  ua-free_MonaghanQualificationRolls1778.html**
  Also available at **http://aharney.us/monaghan/qual-cath.htm**
- Catholic Qualification Rolls Index: County Monaghan
  www.from-ireland.net/catholic-qualification-rolls-monaghan/

Tipperary

- Catholic Inhabitants who swore Oaths of Allegiance to the King in the
  year 1775
  www.igp-web.com/tipperary/oaths/index.htm

Census *see also* Pension Claims & Religious Census

Advice Pages

- Irish Census Records
  www.irishtimes.com/ancestor/browse/records/census/index2.htm
  Introduction.
- Ireland Census
  https://familysearch.org/learn/wiki/en/Ireland_Census
  Detailed advice from the Latter Day Saints.
- Censuses
  www.rootsweb.ancestry.com/~fianna/guide/census.html
  Overview of Irish censuses and census substitutes.
- Your Family Tree: 5. Census Records, Nineteenth Century
  www.proni.gov.uk/no.5_-_19th_century_census__74kb_.pdf

- Your Family Tree: 2: 1901 and 1911 Census
  www.proni.gov.uk/no.2_-_1901_and_1911_census__124kb_.pdf
  Advice from the Public Record Office of Northern Ireland.
- Irish census records date back to 1821, but ...
  www.irish-genealogy-toolkit.com/Irish-census.html
- The Ireland List Census Information Page: Irish Census Returns
  http://freepages.genealogy.rootsweb.ancestry.com/
  ~irelandlist/census.html
- Centenary of 1901 Census of Ireland
  www.lalley.com/index.htm?feature.htm
  General discussion.
- Memorandum on the Fate of the Destroyed Returns of the Census of Ireland 1861-91
  http://homepage.tinet.ie/~seanjmurphy/nai/censusmemo.htm

Link Pages & Lists of Returns
- Availability of Census Returns in Ireland
  www.irishfamilyresearch.co.uk/EssentialResource2.htm
- Actual Censuses
  www.rootsweb.ancestry.com/~fianna/guide/cen1.html
  Details of availability of the 1901 and 1911 censuses, and of fragments from previous censuses.
- Census Online: Ireland
  www.census-online.com/links/Ireland
  Links page.
- Census Links for Ireland
  www.censusfinder.com/ireland.htm
  Gateway; also includes links to sites with trade directories, Griffith's Valuation, baptism registers, etc.
- Online Irish Census Indexes & Records: Ireland Census Records by County: a genealogy guide
  www.genealogybranches.com/irishcensus.html
  Links page.
- Census Returns
  http://freepages.genealogy.rootsweb.ancestry.com/
  ~irishancestors/Census%20returns.html
  Lists surviving returns for early censuses.

Databases
- Pender, Seamus, ed. *A census of Ireland, circa 1659, with supplementary material from the poll money ordinances (1660-1661).* Irish Manuscripts Commission, 1939.
  www.irishmanuscripts.ie/digital/censusofireland1659/index.html
  Digitised book.
- Ireland Census 1821-1851
  http://search.findmypast.ie/search-world-Records/
  ireland-census-1821-1851
  Database of fragments; pay per view.
- Ireland, 1821 Census
  https://familysearch.org/search/collection/2345228
  Database of fragments, with over 275,000 entries. For the 1831 census (over 80,000 entries), see **/2334949.** For 1841 (over 15,000 entries), see **/2346276.** For 1851 (over 58,000 entries), see **/2340880.**
- Ireland: 1841/1851 Census Abstracts (Republic of Ireland)
  http://search.ancestry.co.uk/search/db.aspx?dbid=48493
  Pay per view.
- Census of Ireland 1901/1911 and Census fragments and substitutes, 1821-51
  www.census.nationalarchives.ie
  Includes digitised images of 1901 & 1911 censuses.
- Web: Ireland, Census, 1901
  http://search.ancestry.co.uk/search/db.aspx?dbid=70667
  Pay per view. For the 1911 census, see /db.aspx?dbid=70564

Census Substitutes
A variety of sources are frequently described as census substitutes, although they have nothing to do with the census. These include Griffiths' valuation, the Tithe applotment books, religious censuses, etc. General advice pages include:
- Your Family Tree 14. Seventeenth Century Census Substitutes
  www.proni.gov.uk/no.7_-_17th_century_subs__82kb_.pdf
- Your Family Tree: 6. Census Substitutes, Eighteenth and Nineteenth Century
  www.proni.gov.uk/no.6_-_18th___19th_century_subs__82kb_.pdf

- Eighteenth & Nineteenth Century Census Substitutes
  www.rootsweb.ancestry.com/~irlwem/index3.html
- 19th Century Census Substitutes - Landlord/Tenant Records
  www.irishfamilyresearch.co.uk/essentialresource3.htm
  General introduction to Griffiths' Valuation, the landowners census, tithe applotment books, estate records, etc.

Antrim
- Thinking of Genealogy, Ireland: County Antrim
  www.the-e-site.com/irish/countyantri.htm
  Mainly fragments from the 1851 census.
- Census of Dunaghy: 1851 Census Fragments For Dunaghy, County Antrim, Ireland
  www.ulsterancestry.com/ShowFreePage.php?id=172
- 1901 Census, Co. Antrim
  www.from-ireland.net/1901-census-ireland/antrim
- 1911 Census: Co. Antrim
  www.rootsweb.ancestry.com/~fianna/county/antrim/ant1911.html
  List of Latter Day Saints microfilm.

Armagh
- County Armagh Records
  http://www.igp-web.com/armagh/records.htm
  Scroll down for Pender's 1659 census.
- 1911 Census, Co, Armagh
  www.rootsweb.ancestry.com/~fianna/county/armagh/arm1911.html
  List of Latter Day Saints' microfilms.
- Census of Armagh Town, 1770
  www.ancestryireland.com/family-records/census-of-armagh-town-1770
  Subscription required.
- McConville's Irish Genealogy: the first census of the Fews, 1602
  www.mcconville.org/main/genealogy/census1602.html
  The Fews is a barony in Armagh.

Cavan *See also* Londonderry
- 1821 Census – Cavan
  https://sites.google.com/site/countycavanirelandgenweb/
  census-1821
- Census Abstracts, Co. Cavan, 1821
  www.from-ireland.net/census-abstracts-cavan-1821
  From Drumgoon & Kildrumsherdan
- Census Records: 1821-1891: Surviving Copies, Fragments and Extracts
  http://home.wavecable.com/~colin/genuki/CAV/Census/
  Surviving.htm
  List for Co. Cavan.
- 1911 Census: Co. Cavan
  www.rootsweb.ancestry.com/~fianna/county/cavan/cav1911.html
  List of Latter Day Saints microfilms.
- Drumlomman Parish Cavan Ireland: Census 1821
  www.familyhistory.ie/docs/archives/Drumlomman%20Parish%20 20Census%201821.pdf

Clare
- 1659 Census of Clare
  www.clarelibrary.ie/eolas/coclare/genealogy/pender/
  pender_index.htm
  Census giving the names of the principal occupiers.
- 1901 Census of Population of County Clare
  www.clarelibrary.ie/eolas/coclare/genealogy/1901census/
  1901_clare_census.htm
- 1901 County Clare Census Index
  www.connorsgenealogy.com/clare/#census
- 1911 Census, Co. Clare
  www.rootsweb.ancestry.com/~fianna/county/clare/cla1911.html
  List of Latter Day Saints films
- Clare - 1839 Parish Census - Miltown Malbay
  www.igp-web.com/IGPArchives/ire/clare/census/
  1839-miltown-malbay.txt

  For digitised images, see
  /1images/Miltown_Malbay_Census/index.html

Cork

- Thinking of Genealogy, Ireland: County Cork
  www.the-e-site.com/irish/countycork.htm
  Includes transcripts of the 1766 religious census for many parishes, the
  1821 census for Carrigleigh & Iveleary, & 1901 census for Aghada, Inch
  & Rostellan, etc.
- Names in 1851 Census Records Book, Co. Cork
  http://freepages.genealogy.rootsweb.ancestry.com/~mturner/
  cork/1851_census.htm
- County Cork, Ireland, a Collection of 1851 Census Records
  http://search.ancestry.co.uk/search/db.aspx?dbid=48535
  Pay per view.
- County Cork, Ireland: A Collection of 1851 Census Records
  www.worldvitalrecords.com/indexinfo.aspx?ix=
  gpc0806346108_corkireland1851census
  Pay per view.
- 1911 Census: Co. Cork
  www.rootsweb.ancestry.com/~fianna/county/cork/cor1911.html
  List of films held by the Latter Day Saints.
- Film Numbers, 1901 Ireland Census, County Cork
  www.ginnisw.com/film.htm

Donegal

- 1740 Protestant Householder's Return - Inishowen Parishes
  http://freepages.genealogy.rootsweb.ancestry.com/~donegal/
  1740ph1.htm
- Killymard Parish Census
  http://freepages.genealogy.rootsweb.ancestry.com/
  ~donegal/killymardcen.htm
  Census, 1821.
- Online Census Extracts, Co. Donegal, Ireland
  http://freepages.genealogy.rootsweb.ancestry.com/
  ~donegal/census.htm
  For many places, mainly 1901 and 1911.

Dublin

- The 1851 Dublin City Census, Ireland
  www.worldvitalrecords.com/indexinfo.aspx?ix=eneclann_dcc
  Pay per view.

- Find your ancestors in The 1851 Dublin City Census
  www.findmypast.co.uk/articles/world-records/full-list-of-the-irish-
  family-history-records/census-land-and-substitutes/
  the-index-to-the-dublin-city-census-1851
  Pay per view.
- Find Your Ancestors in Dublin City Census 1901: Rotunda Ward
  www.findmypast.com/articles/world-records/full-list-of-the-
  irish-family-history-records/census-land-and-substitutes/
  dublin-city-census-1901-rotunda-ward
  Pay per view. Also available at
  http://www.worldvitalrecords.com/indexinfo.aspx?ix=eneclann_io0007

Fermanagh

- Census Information
  www.igp-web.com/Fermanagh/Donated.htm#10
  Information from various censuses for Fermanagh, in Excel format.
- Fermanagh, Aughalurcher, 1821, Census
  www.ajmorris.com/dig/toc/ferres.htm
  Scroll down to title. Subscription required. Index only.

Galway See Leitrim

Kerry

- 1659 Census, County Kerry, Ireland
  www.igp-web.com/Kerry/census16a.html
  Pender census.
- 1901 census
  www.igp-web.com/Kerry/census.html
  Co.Kerry; incomplete.
- 1911. Census: County Kerry
  www.igp-web.com/Kerry/census11.html
  Incomplete.
- A Census of the Parishes of Prior and Killemlagh, December 1834
  www.igp-web.com/Kerry/1834text.html
  www.rootsweb.ancestry.com/~irlker/1834text.html

Leitrim

- Leitrim-Roscommon 1901 Census Home Page
  www.leitrim-roscommon.com/1901census
  Covers Galway, Leitrim, Mayo, Roscommon, Sligo, Westmeath, & Wexford.

Limerick

- Connologh Barony, County Limerick: Penders' 1659 Census
  www.countylimerickgenealogy.com/Connologh/index.htm
- 1901 & 1911 Census Householder Listings
  www.limerickcity.ie/Library/LocalStudies/19011911
  CensusHouseholderListings

Londonderry

- 1659 Census, Londonderry City, Co. Derry
  www.from-ireland.net/1659-census-londonderry-derry-city/
- Ireland 1831 and 1841 Census Index
  www.genealogy.com/197facd.html
  Pay per view. Co. Londonderry, 1831, Co. Cavan 1841 only.
- Derry, Desertmartin, Desertmartin 1831 Census Index
  www.ajmorris.com/dig/toc/derres.htm
  Scroll down to title. Subscription required.
- Dreenan, Lavey, County Derry, Ireland: Census of Ireland
  www.dreenan.com
  Click on 'Census' for 1901 & 1911 censuses; also for 1831 censuses for Dreenan and Eden.
- 1831 census: Dunboe Parish, Co. Londonderry
  www.rootsweb.ancestry.com/~nirldy/dunboe/1831cen/1831indx.htm
- Tamlaght O'Crilly parish civil records
  www.torrens.org.uk/Genealogy/BannValley/church/Tamlaght/
  index.html
  1831 census.

Longford

- 1659 Census of Longford
  www.igp-web.com/Longford/longcen.htm

Louth

- 1821 Census, Ardee and Dundalk Town, Co. Louth
  www.from-ireland.net/1821-census-ardee-dundalk-louth

Mayo *See also* Leitrim

- Census and Heads of Households, Co. Mayo, Ireland, 1901 and 1911
  http://freepages.genealogy.rootsweb.ancestry.com/
  ~deesegenes/cen.html
  Many pages for various parishes.
- 1901 census for County Mayo, Ireland: East Mayo
  www.rootsweb.ancestry.com/~fianna/county/mayo/emay1901.html
- 1901 Census for the Parish of Burrishoole
  www.oocities.org/heartland/Park/7461/cens.html

Meath

- People from Meath, Ireland in the 1901 England Census
  www.rootsweb.ancestry.com/~irlmea2/Census/
  1901_england_census.html
- Townland Index
  www.angelfire.com/ak2/ashbourne/townlandlist.html
  Index to Meath 1901 census by townland.

Roscommon *See* Leitrim

Sligo *See also* Leitrim

- Sligo County Ireland 1749 Census
  www.rootsweb.ancestry.com/~irlsli/censussligo1749open.html
- WGW Sligo County, Ireland: The 1901 Census Search Page
  www.rootsweb.ancestry.com/~irlsli/finnsearch.html
- Sligo County Ireland 1901 Census
  www.rootsweb.ancestry.com/~irlsli/sligocensusopenparish.html
  Some transcripts.

Tipperary

- 1821 Census Fragments, County Tipperary
  www.igp-web.com/tipperary/census_1821.htm
- Census 1799: Carrick
  www.igp-web.com/tipperary/1799_carrick.htm

Tyrone
- County Tyrone: Census Records
  www.cotyroneireland.com/menus/census.html
  Includes index to the 1901 census; also various census strays.
  Waterford
- Waterford: Ireland genealogy projects: 1821 Census
  www.igp-web.com/Waterford/census/censusndx.htm
- Waterford Census Records
  www.igp-web.com/IGPArchives/ire/waterford/census.htm
  Primarily extracts from the 1821 census.

Westmeath *See* Leitrim

Wexford *See* Leitrim
- 'The Registered Papers of the Chief Secretary's Office
  www.nationalarchives.ie/topics/Chief_secretary/CSORP.pdf
- Chief Secretary's Office Registered Papers
  www.csorp.nationalarchives.ie
  Digitised images, including name index. Only covers 1818-22 at
  present, but work is in progress on later years.

Church Records
Churches kept a wide variety of records other than those relating to
baptisms, marriages and burials. Relevant websites include:
- The Church of Ireland: genealogy and family history
  http://ireland.anglican.org/information/63
  Notes on parish registers and other sources
- Ireland Church Records
  https://familysearch.org/learn/wiki/en/Ireland_Church_Records
- Church of Ireland Vestry Records
  www.proni.gov.uk/no.2_-_church_of_ireland_vestry_
  records__50kb_.pdf

Armagh
- The Armagh Diocesan Registry Archive
  www.proni.gov.uk/introduction__armagh_diocesan_registry_
  archive.pdf
- Shankill Churchwardens 1653 - 1735
  www.lurganancestry.com/shankillwardens.htm

Down
- Ballynahinch Presbyterian Church 1704-1710
  http://freepages.genealogy.rootsweb.ancestry.com/
  ~rosdavies/WORDS/BallynahinchPresbyDisburse.htm
- Certificates and Testimonials, Recorded in the Presbyterian
  Congregation of Ballynahinch 1715-1734
  http://freepages.genealogy.rootsweb.ancestry.com/~rosdavies/
  WORDS/BallynahinchPresbTestimonials.htm

Londonderry
- Bann Valley Church Records 1796 Garvagh Church Visitation Lists
  www.torrens.org.uk/Genealogy/BannValley/church/GarvaghP1/
  Visits/1796.html

Louth
- County Louth Ireland Genealogical Sources
  www.jbhall.freeservers.com/index.html
  Click on 'Resources' for many pages of parish records, including:
  1855 Ardee Convent Subscription Fund
  1775 Cess Payers of the Parish of Collon
  1890 St. Joseph's Redemptorist Church, Dundalk, Subscription Fund
  1900 Sacred Heart Altar, Haggardstown, Subscribers
  Louth Parish Church Subscription Fund 1890
  1894 Monasterboice Church Building Fund
- Tullyallen New Church
  www.rootsweb.ancestry.com/~fianna/county/louth/loutchu.html
  List of subscribers 1898; over 700 names

Tyrone
- County Tyrone: Church Records
  www.cotyroneireland.com/menus/churchrecord.html
  Includes extracts from a wide range of records, eg seating plans,
  financial statements, lists of elders, confirmations, etc., as well as
  baptisms, marriages and burials.

Ulster
- Home Towns of Ulster Families 1691-1718
  www.lynx2ulster.com/ScotchIrishPioneers/hometowns.php
  List of elders and other prominent Presbyterians, from the records of
  presbyteries and synods

- Introduction to the Clogher Diocesan Records
  www.proni.gov.uk/introduction__clogher_diocesan__web_-2.pdf

Wexford
- Extracts from the Vestry Book of the Parish of Killinick
  www.igp-web.com/IGPArchives/ire/wexford/churches/killinick2.txt

Confirmation Records
- Ireland, Select Catholic Confirmation Registers, 1775-1912
  http://search.ancestry.co.uk/search/db.aspx?dbid=9053
  Pay per view.

- Ginni Swanton's Web Site Confirmation Records: Enniskeane,
  Desertserges and Kinneigh, County Cork
  www.ginnisw.com/confirmation%20Records%20Index.htm

Congregational Records
- Irish Evangelical Society
  www.proni.gov.uk/introduction__irish_evangelical_society.pdf

Corn Census
- 1740 Corn Census of County Louth
  **www.jbhall.freeservers.com/1740_corn_census_of_county_
  louth.htm**

Corporation Records *See* Municipal Records

Coroners Records
- Coroners' inquest papers - what's available?
  **www.proni.gov.uk/index/search_the_archives/proninames/
  coroners__inquest__papers_-_whats_available.htm**

Down
- Inquests 1841 by Coroner's, for Counties & Cities in Ireland
  http://countydown.x10.mx/html/index2.htm
  For Co. Down.

Tipperary
- Tipperary Genealogy: Coroners Inquest
  www.igp-web.com/tipperary/inquests/index.htm
  For 1832-77.

Court Records *see also* Assizes
- Ireland Court Records
  https://familysearch.org/learn/wiki/en/Ireland_Court_Records
- Irish Petty Sessions Courts
  www.irish-genealogy-toolkit.com/irish-petty-sessions.html
- Irish Petty Sessions Court Registers 1828-1912
  **http://search.findmypast.ie/search-world-Records/
  irish-petty-sessions-court-registers-1828-1912**
  Pay per view.

Donegal
- Ardara Petty Sessions Jan 1852 - Dec 1853
  **http://freepages.genealogy.rootsweb.ancestry.com/~donegal/
  pettysessionsardara.htm**

Tipperary
- Petty Sessions Court Records
  www.irelandgenweb.com/irltip/records.htm#court
  www.connorsgenealogy.com/tipp/#court
  For Tipperary, 1851-6.

Deeds
- Ireland Land & Property
  https://familysearch.org/learn/wiki/en/Ireland_Land_and_Property
  Includes sections on the Registry of Deeds, estate records, and
  Valuation Office Revision books.
- Registry of Deeds Service
  www.prai.ie/registry-of-deeds-services
  The registry is able to supply memorials of deeds from 1708.
- Registry of Deeds Index Project Ireland
  **http://freepages.genealogy.rootsweb.ancestry.com/
  ~registryofdeeds/index.html**

- Registry of Deeds
  www.irishtimes.com/ancestor/browse/records/deeds/
  index2.htm#Deeds
- Your Family Tree, 17: Registry of Deeds, Dublin
  www.proni.gov.uk/no.17_-_registry_of_deeds__73kb_.pdf
- Deeds on LDS Film
  http://home.wavecable.com/~colin/genuki/CAV/Deeds/index.html
  From the Registry of Deeds
- Registry of Deeds - Transcripts on LDS Film
  http://home.wavecable.com/~colin/genuki/CAV/Deeds/
  Transcripts.html
- The Land Registry
  www.dfpni.gov.uk/lps/index/land_registration-
  2/the_land_registry.htm
  For Northern Ireland; established 1892.

Cavan
- Deeds on L.D.S. Film
  http://home.wavecable.com/~colin/genuki/CAV/Deeds
  For Co. Cavan, from the Registry of Deeds

Fermanagh
- Fermanagh Deeds (also known as the Brooke deeds)
  www.ulsterancestry.com/ua-BrookeDeeds.html
  18-20th c.

Laois
- The Laois Papers: Deeds
  www.familyhistory.ie/docs/archives/Laois%20Papers%20Deeds.pdf

Diaries
- Index of Persons named in the Lucas Diary, 1740 and 1741
  www.clarelibrary.ie/eolas/coclare/genealogy/
  lucas_diary_names1740_1741.htm
  Names from a Co. Clare diary.
- Introduction: Harshaw Papers
  www.proni.gov.uk/introduction_harshaw_d4149-2.pdf
  Description of the diaries of James Harshaw of Donaghmore,
  mid 19th c. They contain much information on local baptisms, marriages
  and burials

- The Harshaw Diaries
  www.theballards.net/Harshaw

Directories
- Directories
  www.irishtimes.com/ancestor/browse/records/directories/
  index2.htm#Directories
  General introduction, with separate pages on Dublin, Countrywide and
  Provincial directories.
- Find my Past
  www.findmypast.ie
  Includes numerous Directories of Ireland, formerly located at
  www.origins.net
- Street Directories
  www.proni.gov.uk/index/search_the_archives/street_
  directories.htm
  Digitised images of directories held by the Public Record Office of
  Northern Ireland
- Your Family Tree: 9. Street Directories
  www.proni.gov.uk/no.9_-_street_directories__79kb_.pdf
  Advice page from the Public Record Office of Northern Ireland.
- Directories and Almanacs
  www.dublincity.ie/living_in_the_city/libraries/heritage_and_
  history/dublin_and_irish_collections/directories.asp
  In Dublin City Library, but not just relating to Dublin.
- Pigot & Co's Provincial Directory of Ireland 1824
  www.failteromhat.com/pigot.php
- Pigot's Commercial Directory of Ireland, 1824
  www.worldvitalrecords.com/indexinfo.aspx?ix=eneclann_iet0005
  Pay per view.
- Slater's Commercial Directory of Ireland, 1846
  www.failteromhat.com/slater.php
  Also available (pay per view) at
  http://search.findmypast.ie/search-world-Records/
  i-slater-national-commercial-directory-of-ireland-1846.
- Slater's National Commercial Directory of Ireland, 1846
  www.worldvitalrecords.com/indexinfo.aspx?ix=eneclann_iet0010

- Thom's Irish Almanac and Official Directory Of Ireland, 1868
  http://search.findmypast.ie/search-world-Records/thoms-irish-almanac-and-official-directory-of-ireland-1868
  Pay per view.
- Slater's Royal National and Commercial Directory of Ireland, 1870
  www.worldvitalrecords.com/indexinfo.aspx?ix=eneclann_iet0100
  Pay per view.
- Slater's Commercial Directory of Ireland, 1881
  www.worldvitalrecords.com/indexinfo.aspx?ix=eneclann_iet0035
  Pay per view.
- Slater's Royal National Directory of Ireland, 1894
  www.worldvitalrecords.com/indexinfo.aspx?ix=eneclann_iet0084
  Pay per view.
- Ireland, Thom's Directory, 1904
  http://search.ancestry.co.uk/search/db.aspx?dbid=2194
  Pay per view.
- Thom's Official Directory Of Ireland, 1910
  http://search.findmypast.ie/search-world-Records/thoms-official-directory-of-ireland-1910
  Pay per view.
- 1931 Trade Directory, Ireland
  www.from-ireland.net/trade-directory

Antrim

- Bassetts County Antrim 1888 Directory
  www.ajmorris.com/dig/toc/_01dant.htm
  Pay per view. Also available (pay per view) at
  www.worldvitalrecords.com/indexinfo.aspx?ix=eneclann_iet0022.
- MacDonald's Trade Directory 1927 Antrim
  www.familyrelatives.com/search/search_macdonalds_antrim.php
  Pay per view.
- Belfast Street Directories
  www.lennonwylie.co.uk/PDAntrim.htm
  Collection, 1805-1943.
- The Belfast Almanack & Directory 1820
  www.ancestryireland.com/family-records/the-belfast-almanack-directory-1820
  Subscription required.

Armagh

- Dave Jassie's County Armagh Research Material Index: Directories
  http://freepages.genealogy.rootsweb.ancestry.com/~jassie/armagh/Directories
  Collection of trade directory transcripts.
- Genuki: County Armagh: Directories
  www3.ns.sympatico.ca/acauston/genuki/ARM/index.html#Directories
  List, including transcripts from Pigot's 1824, & Slaters 1846, etc.
- MacDonald's Trade Directory 1927 Armagh
  www.familyrelatives.com/search/search_macdonalds_armagh.php
  Pay per view.
- Book of Armagh Directory, 1888
  www.worldvitalrecords.com/indexinfo.aspx?ix=eneclann_iet0023
  Pay per view.
- County Armagh Directory 1888: Armagh City Farmers and Residents
  http://connorsgenealogy.net/Armagh/ArmaghResidentDirectory.htm~
- County Armagh Directory 1888: Armagh City Businesses
  www.connorsgenealogy.net/Armagh/ArmaghCityBusDirectory.htm
- Bradshaw's 1819 Directory for Armagh City
  www.thesilverbowl.com/documents/TABLES/Bradshaw%20Armagh%201812%20TABLE%20format.htm
- City of Armagh - Directories - Pigot, 1824
  http://www3.ns.sympatico.ca/acauston/genuki/ARM/Armagh/ArmaghPigot1824.html
- Directories and Trade Records for Lurgan
  www.lurganancestry.com/directories.htm
  Includes extracts from various directories, 1819-1959.
- Directory of Lurgan Residents 1819
  www.ancestryireland.com/family-records/directory-of-lurgan-residents-1819

Carlow

- Index to Carlow Trade Directories
  www.rootsweb.ancestry.com/~irlcar2/Directories.htm
  Extracts from many directories.
- 1788 Lucas' General Directory of the Kingdom of Ireland
  www.from-ireland.net/1788-lucas-directory-dublin-richard-lucas
  Entries relating to Co's Carlow, Kilkenny, Laois & Limerick.

Clare

- Clare Local Studies project
  www.clarelibrary.ie/eolas/library/local-studies/clasp/index.htm
  Includes Lucas's Directory, 1788: Ennis; Guy's Directory, 1893;
  Hogan's Directories of Kilkee 1842, 1863; Pigot's Directory, Clare,
  1824; Slater's Directory, Clare, 1846; Bassett's Directory, Clare, 1875-6
  & 1880-81.
- Online Records
  www.clarelibrary.ie/eolas/coclare/genealogy/genealog.htm
  Includes 1893 Guy's Directory, Clare; 1881 Slater's Directory, Ennis &
  Clarecastle; 1880-1 Bassett's Directory, Clare; 1875-6 Bassett's
  Directory, Clare; 1870, Slater's Directory, Ennis & Clarecastle; 1842,
  1863 Hogan's Directory, Kilkee; 1846 Slater's Directory, Clare; 1814
  Leet's Directory, Clare; 1824 Pigot's Directory, Clare; 1788 Lucas's
  Directory, Ennis.

Cork

- Historical Directories
  www.corkpastandpresent.ie/places/streetandtradedirectories
  Includes many directories for Co. Cork, 1753-1945.
- Holden's Triennial Directory Cork, 1809
  www.failteromhat.com/holdens/holden.php
- Post Office General Directory of Cork 1842-43
  www.failteromhat.com/cork1842.php
- Henry and Coughlan's General Directory of Cork, 1867
  www.worldvitalrecords.com/indexinfo.aspx?ix=eneclann_iet0012
  Pay per view. Also covers other counties in the Province of Munster.
- Francis Guy's County and City of Cork, Ireland, Directory, 1875 – 1876
  www.worldvitalrecords.com/indexinfo.aspx?ix=ia_
  francisguyscount00guycuoft_1
- Guys Postal Directory 1914 for County Cork, Ireland
  www.failteromhat.com/guy.php
  For Cork City, see /guy1914.php
- Directory of Cork City 1787
  www.failteromhat.com/lucas1787.php
- Ginni Swanton's Web Site: Cork City Directory 1875
  www.ginnisw.com/Cork%20City%20Directory/Thumb/Thumbs1.htm

- Various Directories In The Bandon Area
  www.bandon-genealogy.com/local-directories.htm

Donegal

- Donegal Directories
  http://freepages.genealogy.rootsweb.ancestry.com/~donegal/
  directory.htm
  Includes Pigot's, 1824, Slater's 1846 & 1857, & Donegal entries for the
  Derry almanac, 1903.
- Donegal County Directory for 1862: From Thom's Almanac and Official
  Directory for the Year 1862.
  www.libraryireland.com/articles/
  DonegalCountyDirectoryThom1862/index.php

Down

- County Down Guide and Directory, 1886
  www.worldvitalrecords.com/indexinfo.aspx?ix=eneclann_iet0025
  Pay per view.

Dublin

- The Dublin Directories (1636-1900)
  www.microform.co.uk/guides/R97605.pdf
  Guide to a collection published on microfilm
- Dublin Directories on Microfilm
  www.dublincity.ie/main-menu-services-recreation-culture-dublin-
  city-public-libraries-and-archive-heritage-and-histor-2
  List.
- Wilson's 1820 Dublin Directory
  www.from-ireland.net/wilsons-1820-dublin-directory
- Pettigrew and Oulton's Dublin Directory 1838
  www.ajmorris.com/dig/toc/_01du38.htm
  Pay per view.
- Pettigrew and Oulton's Dublin Almanac 1842
  www.failteromhat.com/dublin1842.htm
- Shaw's Dublin City Directory 1850
  www.dublin1850.com/dublin1850
- Dublin City Directory 1850
  www.libraryireland.com/DublinDirectory1850/a.php

- Porter's Guide and Directory for North County Dublin 1912
  www.dublin1850.com/porter1912/intro.html

Fermanagh
- Trade Directories
  www.igp-web.com/Fermanagh/Donated.htm#3
  Many pages from Co. Fermanagh directories, in Excel format.
- Find your ancestors in MacLoskie's Directory Of Fermanagh 1848
  www.findmypast.com/articles/world-records/full-list-of-the-irish-family-history-records/newspapers-directories-and-social-history/macloskie-directory-of-fermanagh-1848
  Pay per view.
- Ireland, County Fermanagh Directory and Household Almanac 1880
  www.ajmorris.com/dig/toc/_01ferm.htm
  Pay per view.

Kerry
- MacDonald's Irish Trade Directory 1927 Kerry
  www.familyrelatives.com/search/search_macdonalds_kerry.php
  Pay per view.

Kildare
- Slater's Trade Directory for Co. Kildare, 1846.
  www.kildare.ie/library/slaters-directory-1846/index.asp
- Thom's Trade Directories, 1849 and 1854
  http://kildare.ie/library/Thoms-Directories/index.asp
  Of Co Kildare.

Kilkenny *See also* Carlow & Waterford
- Kilkenny Directory Records
  www.igp-web.com/IGPArchives/ire/kilkenny/directory.htm
  Includes 'Directory for the Year 1788 (City of Kilkenny)', & '1824 Pigot Directory of Leixlip'.
- Kilkenny City and County Guide and Directory, 1884
  www.worldvitalrecords.com/indexinfo.aspx?ix=eneclann_iet0021

Laois *see* Carlow
- 1931 Trade Directory, Co. Laois
  www.from-ireland.net/trade-directory/laois

Limerick *see also* Carlow
- Trades & Street Directories, 1769-1976
  www.limerickcity.ie/Library/LocalStudies/TradesStreetDirectories1769-1976
  Digitised images of many Co Limerick directories.
- A General Directory of the Kingdom of Ireland 1788: Limerick
  www.celticcousins.net/ireland/lim1788.htm
- Pigot's Directory of Ireland 1824: Limerick
  www.celticcousins.net/ireland/1824limerick.htm
- Limerick City and County Directory, 1880
  www.worldvitalrecords.com/indexinfo.aspx?ix=eneclann_ie0073
  Pay per view.
- Ferrar's Limerick Directory of 1769
  www.celticcousins.net/ireland/lim.htm
  City only.
- Limerick City Directory 1788: an extract from the General directory of the Kingdom of Ireland, 1788
  www.geocities.ws/irishancestralpages/limdir1788main.html
- Find your ancestors in Guy's Limerick Directory, 1912
  www.findmypast.com/articles/world-records/full-list-of-the-irish-family-history-records/newspapers-directories-and-social-history/guys-limerick-directory-1912
  Pay per view.

Londonderry
- MacDonald's Trade Directory 1927 Londonderry
  www.familyrelatives.com/search/search_macdonalds_londonderry.php
  Pay per view.

Longford
- The Genealogy of County Longford, Ireland: Directories
  www.igp-web.com/Longford/directories.htm
  Includes 1894 Longford Town Directory, 1824 Longford Town Directory, 1824 Granard Town Directory, & 1892 Longford Almanac & Directory.

Louth
- Louth County Guide and Directory, 1886
  www.worldvitalrecords.com/indexinfo.aspx?ix=eneclann_iet0024
  Pay per view.

Mayo

- Castlebar, Co. Mayo – Pigots Directory 1824
  www.swilson.info/wp/?p=1090
- Castlebar, Co. Mayo, Ireland Directory 1846 incomplete
  http://freepages.genealogy.rootsweb.ancestry.com/
  ~deesegenes/cas.html~

Munster

- Find your ancestors in Guy's Directory Of Munster 1893
  www.findmypast.com/articles/world-records/full-list-of-the-irish-
  family-history-records/newspapers-directories-and-social-
  history/guys-directory-of-munster-1893
  Pay per view. Covers Co's Clare, Cork, Kerry, Limerick, Tipperary, &
  Waterford.

Offaly

- Offaly (King's Co.) Directory Records
  www.igp-web.com/IGPArchives/ire/offaly/directory.htm
  Includes extracts from an 1823 directory for Banagher, Birr, Frankford,
  Philipstown, & Tullamore.

Tipperary *See also* Munster

- Tipperary Directories
  www.igp-web.com/tipperary/directory/index.htm
  Includes extracts from directories of 1787, 1824, 1856 & 1889.
- Bassett's Directory of Co. Tipperary, 1889
  http://homepage.eircom.net/~rareclonmel/Tipperary1889.htm
- 1889 Tipperary Directory
  www.irelandgenweb.com/irltip/Records/1889Directory.htm
- MacDonald's Trade Directory 1927 Tipperary
  www.familyrelatives.com/search/search_macdonalds_tipperary.php
  Pay per view.

Tyrone

- County Tyrone: Trade Directories
  www.cotyroneireland.com/menus/trade.html
  Includes extracts from numerous 19th c. directories.

- Tyrone Directories
  www.igp-web.com/IGPArchives/ire/tyrone/directories.htm
  Extract for Cookstown, from The Belfast And Ulster Towns Directory,
  1910.

Ulster

- The Belfast and Province of Ulster Directory, 1852-1900
  www.worldvitalrecords.com/indexinfo.aspx?ix=eneclann_iet0011
  Pay per view.
- Ulster Directory, 1900
  www.ancestryireland.com/family-records/ulster-directory-1900/
  Subscription required.
- Ulster Towns Directory 1910
  www.libraryireland.com/UlsterDirectory1910/Contents.php

Waterford *See also* Munster

- 1824 Waterford Directories
  www.igp-web.com/Waterford/directories/index.htm
  Extracts from Pigot's 1824 Directory for Lismore, Cappoquin, &
  Kilmacthomas.

- Find your ancestors in Harvey's Waterford Almanac and Directory For
  1866
  www.findmypast.com/articles/world-records/full-list-of-the-irish-
  family-history-records/newspapers-directories-and-social-
  history/harveys-waterford-almanac-and-directory-for-1866
  Pay per view.
- Waterford Directory 1894
  www.lennonwylie.co.uk/1894WaterfordDirectory.htm

Wexford

- Wexford County Guide and Directory, 1885
  www.worldvitalrecords.com/indexinfo.aspx?ix=eneclann_iet0026
  Pay per view.

DNA

- Irish Genealogical Toolkit: Genealogy DNA testing
  www.irish-genealogy-toolkit.com/genealogy-dna-testing.html

- Irish DNA Atlas Project
  www.familyhistory.ie/index.php/en/2012-04-22-23-12-47
- North of Ireland Family History Society: DNA Project
  www.nifhs.org/documents/NIFHS_DNA_Project.pdf

Dog Licences

- Ireland Dog Licence Registers
  www.findmypast.com/articles/world-records/full-list-of-the-irish-family-history-records/institutions-and-organisations/ireland-dog-licence-registers
  Over, 6,000,000 names, late 19th c. Pay per view.

Carlow

- Bagenalstown Dog Licences 1870
  www.rootsweb.com/~irlcar2/Licences_1.htm

Donegal

- Registry of Dogs Licence Book, Petty Sessions District of Dunfanaghy, Co Donegal: First 200 Dogs Officially Licenced 1866
  http://freepages.genealogy.rootsweb.ancestry.com/~donegal/dunfanaghydoglicences.htm

Electoral Registers, Pollbooks, & Freeholders' Records
Freeholders were voters, so their records are equivalent to electoral registers.

- Your Family Tree: 10. Voters, Poll and Freeholders' Records
  www.proni.gov.uk/no.10_-_voters__poll___freeholders_records__74kb_.pdf
  Advice page from the Public Record Office of Northern Ireland.
- About Electoral Registers for Ireland 1832-38
  blog.findmypast.co.uk/articles/about-electoral-registers-for-ireland-1832-38
  Pay per view.
- Illiterate Voters in Irish Boroughs in 1837
  www.ancestryireland.com/family-records/illiterate-voters-in-irish-boroughs-in-1837
  Subscription required.

- Find your ancestors in Reports From Committees, Fictitious Votes (Ireland), Select Committee On Fictitious Votes, 1837-1838
  www.findmypast.com/articles/world-records/full-list-of-the-irish-family-history-records/census-land-and-substitutes/reports-from-committees-fictitious-votes-ireland-select-committee-on-fictitious-votes-1837-1838
  Lists voters. Pay per view. Also available (pay per view) at
  www.worldvitalrecords.com/indexinfo.aspx?ix=eneclann_iet0101.
- Freeholders Records
  www.proni.gov.uk/index/search_the_archives/freeholders_records.htm
  Discussion of a source which lists those entitled to vote, or who did vote. Includes database.

Antrim

- Freeholders Registered to Vote in the Elections, Co Antrim 1776
  www.ancestryireland.com/family-records/freeholders-registered-to-vote-in-the-elections-co-antrim-1776
  Subscription required.
- 1790 Electoral Lists for Co. Antrim
  www.ballymoneyancestry.com/1790_-electoral-lists.aspx
- Voters for Clements Monepenny – 1744
  www.igp-web.com/IGPArchives/ire/antrim/xmisc/voters-1744.txt
  From the Town Book of the Corporation of Belfast.

Armagh

- A List of Notices to Register Freeholds at Armagh
  http://freepages.genealogy.rootsweb.ancestry.com/~donaghmore1/armfrhldlst.html
  In 1830.
- Applications to Register as Voters in the Borough of Armagh
  www.ancestryireland.com/family-records/applications-to-register-as-voters-in-the-barony-of-armagh
  Subscription site. For 1839.
- Applicants for Right to Vote, Armagh Barony, Co. Armagh, 1839
  www.ancestryireland.com/family-records/applicants-for-right-to-vote-armagh-barony-co-armagh-1839
  Subscription required.

Carlow

- Carlow Freeholders, 1767
  www.from-ireland.net/carlow-freeholders-1767
- County of Carlow: An Alphabetical List of Persons who have Registered their Votes to ... 1838
  www.rootsweb.com/~irlcar2/1838_voters.htm
- Carlow County: Notice to Register Votes 1846
  www.rootsweb.ancestry.com/~irlcar2/Register_Votes_1846_00.htm
- Register of Electors 1920-1921: Absent Voters Lists Parliamentary County of Carlow
  www.rootsweb.ancestry.com/~irlcar2/absent_voters_1.htm
- Irish Free State Army Absent Voters List circa 1926: Constituency of Carlow-Kilkenny, County of Carlow
  www.rootsweb.ancestry.com/~irlcar2/postal_voters.htm
- Borough of Carlow: Voters registered in the Borough: Appendix 6 of the First report from the Select Committee on Fictitious Votes, Ireland Printed 12 May 1837.
  www.rootsweb.ancestry.com/~irlcar2/1837_voters_list.htm
- County of Carlow: an Alphabetical List of Persons Who Have Registered their Votes
  www.rootsweb.ancestry.com/~irlcar2/1838_voters.htm
  Digitised image of printed list, 1838.
- Irish Free State Army: Absent Voters List circa 1926: Constituency of Carlow-Kilkenny. County of Carlow
  www.rootsweb.ancestry.com/~irlcar2/postal_voters.htm
- Carlow Electors Register of 1936/37
  www.rootsweb.com/~irlcar2/1937.htm
  For Carlow Town.

Cavan

- County Cavan Poll Book, 1791
  **https://sites.google.com/site/countycavanirelandgenweb/
  poll-book-1791**
- 1826 General Election, Name Index, Co. Cavan
  www.from-ireland.net/1826-general-election-records-cavan

Clare

- Freeholders of County Clare, 1768
  **www.clarelibrary.ie/eolas/coclare/genealogy/don_tran/regs/
  freeholders_county_clare_1768.htm**
- List of Freeholders [including landlords and tenants]: County of Clare, 1821
  **www.clarelibrary.ie/eolas/coclare/genealogy/
  freeholders_1821/list_of_freeholders_1821.htm**
- Registry of Freeholders 1829 for the County of Clare
  **www.clarelibrary.ie/eolas/coclare/genealogy/don_tran/regs/
  freeholders_co_clare1829.htm**
- Index to Freeholders Registered to Vote at Elections, Co. Clare, 1829
  **www.ancestryireland.com/family-records/index-to-freeholders-
  registered-to-vote-at-elections-co-clare-1829/**
  Subscription required.
- Applicants to the Registry of Freeholders, Co. Clare, 1841
  **www.clarelibrary.ie/eolas/coclare/genealogy/freeholders_1841/
  registry_1841_index.htm**
- County of Clare, Ireland: Freeholders List for Ibrickane Barony
  www.igp-web.com/Clare/freeholdersofclare.html

Donegal

- Freeholders Registered to Vote in the Elections, Co. Donegal 1767-1771
  **www.ancestryireland.com/family-records/freeholders-
  registered-to-vote-in-the-elections-co-donegal-1767-1771**
  Subscription required.
- Applications to Register Freeholds in the Barony of Banagh, Co Donegal, 1829-31
  **http://freepages.genealogy.rootsweb.ancestry.com/~donegal/
  banaghfreeholders.htm**

  There are similar pages for the baronies of
  Boylagh, **/boylaghfreeholders.htm**
  Ennishowen, **/Inishowenfreeholders.htm**
  Kilmacrenan, **/kilmacfreeholders.htm**
  Raphoe, **/raphoefreeholders.htm**
  Tirhugh, **/tirhughfreeholders.htm**

Down

- List of Applications received by the Clerk of the Peace of the County of Down, since the last General Quarter Sessions, to Register Freeholds at Newry, in said County.
**http://freepages.genealogy.rootsweb.ancestry.com/
~donaghmore1/newfrhldapp.html**
In 1830. For Upper Iveagh, see **/upivfrhldapp.html;**
for Lower Iveagh, **/lowiveaghfrhld.html;** for Ards, **/ards.htm**
- Newry Electors, 1868
www.ancestryireland.com/family-records/newry-electors-1868
Subscription required.

Dublin

- Dublin City Library and Archive: Electoral lists 1908 to 1912, 1915
http://dublinheritage.ie/burgesses/index.php
For 1939-40, see /electoral/index.php.

Fermanagh

- Poll of Electors 1788
www.rootsweb.ancestry.com/~nirfer/1788_poll.htm
For Co.Fermanagh.
- 1747-1768 Freeholders List of Electors
www.rootsweb.ancestry.com/~nirfer/1747-1768freeholders.html
For Co. Fermanagh.
- Freeholders registered to vote in the elections, Co. Fermanagh, 1747-1768
**www.ancestryireland.com/family-records/freeholders-registered-
to-vote-in-the-elections-co-fermanagh-1747-1768**
Subscription required.

Kerry

- 1926 Register of Electors Killarney Urban W
www.igp-web.com/Kerry/elkill1.html
www.rootsweb.ancestry.com/~irlker/elkill1.html
For religious, see **/relnames.html**

Kildare

- Voters Register 1835 – 1839: Qualifying Freeholders and Leaseholders: Extracted from the *Leinster Express*
**http://kildare.ie/Library/KildareCollectionsandResearchServices/
votersregister/index.asp**

Kilkenny

- Kilkenny: Electors for the Polling District of Callan, 1896
**www.igp-web.com/IGPArchives/ire/kilkenny/xmisc/callan-elec-
1896.txt**

Limerick

- Registers of Electors
www.limerickcity.ie/Library/LocalStudies/RegistersOfElectors
For Limerick, 1885, 1923, 1931, 1940, 1945, & 1950.

- Franchise and Elections, 1869-1954
**www.limerick.ie/historicalresources/limerickcityarchives/
archivecollections/digitalarchives/limerickcitycouncilandlocal
governmentcollections/franchiseandelections1869-1954**
A variety of registers.
- 1817 Election (report & electors lists)
**www.limerickcity.ie/Library/LocalStudies/1817Election
reportelectorslists/**
For Limerick city.
- 1829 Freeholders in Limerick City and environs (the County of the City of Limerick)
**www.limerickcity.ie/Library/LocalStudies/1829Freeholdersin
LimerickCityandenvironstheCountyoftheCityofLimerick**
- 1837 Electoral List
www.limerickcity.ie/Library/LocalStudies/1837ElectoralList
For Limerick city.
- Analysis of the Late Election of Limerick, 1852
**www.limerickcity.ie/Library/LocalStudies/AnalysisoftheLate
lectionofLimerick1852**

Louth

- 1822 County Louth Freeholders
www.jbhall.freeservers.com/louth_freeholders.htm
Also 1824.

- County Louth Freeholders 1822
  www.rootsweb.ancestry.com/~fianna/county/louth/loufree1822.html
  Continued for L-Z at **/loufre2.html.**
- 1824 County Louth Freeholders (supplementary list)
  www.rootsweb.ancestry.com/~fianna/county/louth/loufree1824.html
- 1842 County Louth Voters List
  www.jbhall.freeservers.com/1842_county_louth_voters.htm
- 1865 County Louth Voters' List
  www.jbhall.freeservers.com/1865_voters_list.htm
- 1832 Dundalk Voters' List
  www.jbhall.freeservers.com/1832_dundalk_voters.htm

Tipperary
- Index to Freeholders Registered to Vote at Elections, Co. Tipperary, 1775
  www.ancestryireland.com/family-records/index-to-freeholders-registered-to-vote-at-elections-co-tipperary-1775
  Subscription required.
- List Index to Freeholders Registered to Vote at Elections, Co. Tipperary, 1775 of Freeholders of the County of Tipperary in the year 1776
  www.igp-web.com/tipperary/freeholders/index.htm

Tyrone
- Freeholders' Records 1829-1832
  www.cotyroneireland.com/menus/freeholders.html
  Applications to register freeholds for Ardstraw, Bodoney, Camus, Cappagh, Donagheady, Leckpatrick, Termonmaguirk & Urney.

Westmeath
- Westmeath, Athlone Voters List – 1861
  www.igp-web.com/IGPArchives/ire/westmeath/censubs/voters.txt

Wexford
- Wexford Miscellaneous Records
  www.igp-web.com/IGPArchives/ire/wexford/misc.htm
  Includes various lists of freemen registered to vote, etc., especially in 1835.

Emigrant Savings Bank
The Bank was founded by the Irish Emigrant Society for the Irish in New York.
- Emigrant Savings Bank Test Books: Brief Background
  www.pefagan.com/gen/flan/flnembn1.htm
- New York Emigrant Savings Bank, 1850-1883
  http://search.ancestry.com/search/db.aspx?htx=List&dbid=8760

Emigration *See also* Transportation
There are numerous sites devoted to emigration - especially those giving passenger lists. Sites which deal with just one journey are not listed here as there are far too many. For general introductions, see:
- Irish Emigration
  www.irish-genealogy-toolkit.com/Irish-emigration.html
- Introduction to Passenger List Research
  www.rootsweb.ancestry.com/~fianna/migrate/pass.html
- Ireland Emigration and Immigration
  https://familysearch.org/learn/wiki/en/Ireland_Emigration_and_Immigration
- Your Family Tree: 11. Emigration Records
  www.proni.gov.uk/no.11_-_emigration__74kb_.pdf
  Advice page from the Public Record Office of Northern Ireland.
- Irish Abroad
  www.irishabroad.com/yourroots
  Includes various guides & resources, including a passenger list database. Subscription required.
- Emigration
  www.irishtimes.com/ancestor/browse/emigration/lists/#emigration/
  Click 'Emigration', for bibliographies on emigration to North & South America, Europe, Australasia, & South Africa; also 'Published Passenger and Emigrant Lists'.

Many pages provide bibliographies of published works, and links to web pages. See:
- Immigration Bibliography
  www.rootsweb.ancestry.com/~fianna/migrate/sources.html
  Immigrants to North America.

- Irish Passenger Lists Research Guide: Finding Ship Passenger & Immigration Records, Ireland to America: a bibliography of books, CD-Roms, Microfilm, & Online Records
  www.genealogybranches.com/irishpassengerlists/index.html
- A Bibliography of Ship Passenger Lists, 1538-1825
  www.rootsweb.ancestry.com/~fianna/migrate/lancour.html
- Passenger Lists and Immigration 1700-1800
  www.rootsweb.ancestry.com/~fianna/migrate/passearly.html
  Book list for U.S. and North American migration.
- Introduction to Passenger List Research
  www.rootsweb.ancestry.com/~fianna/migrate/pass.html
  Continued at **/pass2.html.**
- Published Passenger and Emigrant Lists
  www.irishtimes.com/ancestor/browse/emigration/lists/#emigration
  Lists in print.
- Ship and Passenger Lists and Such
  www.rootsweb.ancestry.com/~fianna/migrate/index.html
  Introduction, with many links.
- Ship Passenger Lists and Records Online: Internet Sources for Digitized or Transcribed Passenger Records & Indexes   http
  www.germanroots.com/onlinelists.html
  Links page.
- Passenger Lists arranged by Century and Destination
  www.rootsweb.ancestry.com/~fianna/migrate/shiplists.html
  Gateway for Irish lists.
- The Ships List
  www.theshipslist.com/index.html
  Numerous pages of transcripts etc.
- Roots Ireland: Ship Passenger Lists
  www.rootsireland.ie/index.php?id=70
  Pay per view database.
- Documenting Ireland: Parliament, People and Migration
  www.dippam.ac.uk
  Includes the 'Irish Emigration Database', and 'Voices of Migration and Return'.
- Immigrant Ships Transcribers Guild
  www.immigrantships.net
  Transcripts of passenger lists from many ships.
- L.D.S. Records on Irish Migration
  www.rootsweb.ancestry.com/~fianna/migrate/ldse.html
  List of Latter Day Saints resources.
- Passenger Lists leaving UK 1890-1960
  search.findmypast.co.uk/search-world-Records/passenger-lists-leaving-uk-1890-1960
- Irish Passenger Lists
  http://members.tripod.com/~Data_Mate/irish/Irish.htm
  Numerous transcripts.
- Irish Passenger Lists, 1803 - 1806
  www.worldvitalrecords.com/indexinfo.aspx?ix=gpc_irishpassengerlists1803-1806
  Pay per view.
- Irish Passenger Lists, 1847-1871
  http://search.ancestry.co.uk/search/db.aspx?dbid=48579
  Pay per view. Also available (pay per view) at
  www.worldvitalrecords.com/indexinfo.aspx?ix=gpc_irishpassengerlists1847-1871
- Olive Tree Genealogy
  www.rootsweb.ancestry.com/~ote
  Passenger list database.
- Ireland Passenger Lists, 1858-1870
  www.worldvitalrecords.com/indexinfo.aspx?ix=eneclann_enec010
  Pay per view.
- Immigration and Travel
  www.findmypast.ie/articles/help-and-advice/genealogy-in-ireland/6-immigration-and-travel
  Database including Passenger Lists Leaving UK 1890-1960, & Transportation Migration Index listing Irish passengers to America, 1858-70.

Emigration to Specific Places

Australia
- Home-coming Series, 3: Emigration to Australia
  www.proni.gov.uk/ no.2_-_emigration_to_australia__32kb_.pdf
  Records held by the Public Record Office of Northern Ireland.

- Mallow Archaeological & Historical Society: Famine Orphans from County Cork to Australia
  www.rootsweb.ancestry.com/~irlmahs/morph.htm

Canada See also United States
- Immigrants to Canada
  http://jubilation.uwaterloo.ca/~marj/genealogy/thevoyage.html
  General introduction to 19th century migration, with many links.
- Immigration/Migration Records: Atlantic Provinces, Canada
  www.rootsweb.ancestry.com/~fianna/oc/canada/can-nb.html
- Home-coming Series, 2: Emigration to Canada
  www.proni.gov.uk/no.3_-_emigration_to_canada__34kb_.pdf
  Records held by the Public Record Office of Northern Ireland.
- Find your ancestors in Parliamentary Papers, Emigration (Canada) Canadian Emigration: 1826 Parliamentary Papers
  www.findmypast.com/articles/world-records/full-list-of-the-irish-family-history-records/immigration-and-travel/canadian-emigration-1826-parliamentary-papers
  Identifies Irish settlers in Canada. Pay per view.
- Library and Archives Canada: Irish
  www.bac-lac.gc.ca/eng/discover/immigration/history-ethnic-cultural/Pages/irish.aspx
  Research guidance for the major Canadian repository.
- Moving Here, Staying Here: the Canadian Immigrant Experience
  www.collectionscanada.gc.ca/immigrants/index-e.html
- Grosse-Île in Quebec: the last resting place for over 6,000 Irish souls
  www.moytura.com/grosse-ile.htm
  General discussion; no names.
- Immigrants at Grosse Île Quarantine Station, 1832-1937
  www.bac-lac.gc.ca/eng/discover/immigration/immigration-records/immigrants-grosse-ile-1832-1937/Pages/immigrants-grosse-ile.aspx
  Database.
- West Ireland Emigration to Canada
  www.teamapproach.ca/irish
- New Brunswick Irish Portal
  archives.gnb.ca/APPS/PrivRecs/IrishFamine
  Includes various migration databases.

- Prince Edward Island Data Pages: Irish born in PE1 before 1846
  http://homepages.rootsweb.ancestry.com/~mvreid/pei/peirish.html

England
- Moving Here: Tracing Your Roots: Irish Roots
  http://webarchive.nationalarchives.gov.uk/+/
  http://www.movinghere.org.uk/galleries/roots/irish/irish.htm
  The Irish in England.
- Hibernia
  http://freepages.genealogy.rootsweb.ancestry.com/~hibernia/
  index.htm
  Irish in the Liverpool area; includes birth, marriage and burial indexes.
- Irish Families in Liverpool Parish Records
  www.ancestry.com/cs/Satellite?childpagename=USLearning
  Center%2FLearning_C%2FPageDefault&pagename=
  LearningWrapper&cid=1265125521712

New Zealand
- New Zealand Ireland Connection
  www.otago.ac.nz/historyarthistory/nzic

South America
- Society for Irish Latin American Studies
  www.irishargentine.org
  Includes various databases.

Spain
- The Irish in Spanish Archives
  www.irishancestors.ie/?page_id=926

United States See also Canada
- Ancestor Search: United States Passenger Lists Genealogy Searches
  www.searchforancestors.com/records/passenger_tousa.html
  Includes links to several Irish passenger list databases.
- 19th Century Emigration to the North Americas
  www.proni.gov.uk/index/exhibitions_talks_and_events/
  19th_century_emigration_to_the_north_america_online.htm

- Home-coming Series: 1: Emigration to USA
  www.proni.gov.uk/no.1_-_emigration_to_usa__38kb_.pdf
  Records held by the Public Record Office of Northern Ireland
- US & Canada: Passenger and Immigration Lists Index 1500s-1900s
  http://search.ancestry.com/search/db.aspx?dbid=7486
  Pay per view
- Dunbrody Famine Ship and Irish Emigrant Experience: Emigration
  Database
  www.dunbrody.com/get-involved/irish-emigration-database
  Covers arrivals at New York, 1846-90; arrivals at Boston, Baltimore,
  New Orleans, and Philadelphia, 1846-51.
- Famine: Irish Passenger Record Datafile
  http://aad.archives.gov/aad/fielded-search.jsp?dt=180&tf=F&cat=all
  Arrivals at New York, 1846-51. These are also given (pay per view) at:
  www.familyrelatives.com/search/us_search/search_
  usairishfamine.php
  search.ancestry.co.uk/search/db.aspx?dbid=5969
  www.worldvitalrecords.com/indexinfo.aspx?ix=ireland_famine
- Emigration Lists from Irish Ports to North America: passenger lists from
  Ireland
  www.ulsterancestry.com/ua-free_Passenger_Lists_1815.
  htmlc.1815-16
- Transatlantic Migration From North America To Britain & Ireland 1858-
  1870
  http://search.findmypast.ie/search-world-Records/transatlantic-
  migration-from-north-america-to-britain-and-ireland-1858-1870
  Pay per view.
- The Famine: Immigrants
  www.lalley.com
  Click on 'Passengers' for various passenger lists to New York and New
  Castle, Delaware.

- New Ships Database Extraction Tool
  www.cimorelli.com/safe/shipmenu.htm See also **</irishpass.html**
  Collection of databases relating to US immigrants; scroll down for 'Irish
  immigrants'

- Irish Immigrants to North America 1803-1871
  www.genealogy.com/257facd.html
  Presumably from published sources; subscription required.
- The Irish Emigration Database
  www.qub.ac.uk/cms/collection/IED.htm
  Migration to North America, 18-19th c.
- The Olive Tree Genealogy: Irish Immigration to U.S.A. & Canada
  www.olivetreegenealogy.com/ships/irishtousa.shtml
  Includes various databases, some pay per view.
- Ship Passenger Lists from Ireland to America: miscellaneous ships
  http://search.ancestry.co.uk/search/db.aspx?dbid=6138
  Pay per view.
- Ships from Ireland to Early America, 1623-1850
  http://search.ancestry.co.uk/search/db.aspx?htx=
  BookList&dbid=49362
  Pay per view.
- Irish Emigrants in North America, Part Four and Part Five
  http://search.ancestry.co.uk/search/db.aspx?htx=
  BookList&dbid=49203
  Pay per view. Covers, c.1775-1825. For Part 6 [1670-1830], see =49204.
- Irish Emigrants in North America [1775-1825]
  http://search.ancestry.co.uk/search/db.aspx?dbid=49202
  Pay per view.
- Chicago Irish Families 1875-1925
  www.reocities.com/Heartland/Park/7461/chicago.html
- Chicago Irish Genealogy and History
  www.chicagoirishgenealogy.com
- The Irish in Iowa
  www.celticcousins.net/irishiniowa
- Irish Immigrants in Baltimore
  http://teaching.msa.maryland.gov/000001/000000/000131/
  html/t131.html
- The Irish in Nineteenth Century New York and beyond
  http://freepages.genealogy.rootsweb.ancestry.com/~nyirish/
  research.html

- The Famine Immigrants: lists of Irish Immigrants arriving at the Port of New York 1846-1851 ... Ships that sailed from Port of Galway to Port of New York
  www.celticcousins.net/ireland/galwayships.htm
  Continued at **/galwayships2.htm**
- Irish Individuals in New York City Almshouse
  http://allenglishrecords.com/ireland/almshouse-a.shtml
  List, 19th c. Continued at /almshouse-ireland.shtml
- New York - Irish Genealogy
  http://freepages.genealogy.rootsweb.ancestry.com/~irishancestors/ NewYork.html
  Links page.
- Immigration of Irish Quakers to Pennsylvania, 1682-1750
  http://search.ancestry.co.uk/search/db.aspx?dbid=48483
  Pay per view. Also available (pay per view) at
  www.worldvitalrecords.com/indexinfo.aspx?ix=ia_ immigrationofiri00myer
- The Museum of Newport Irish History: The Official Site of Irish History for Newport, Rhode Island
  http://newportirishhistory.org
- Irish Immigrants to 17th century Virginia
  www.ulsterancestry.com/ua-free-Irish_Immigrants_17th- cty_Virginia.html

Emigration from Specific Places

Antrim
- Emigrants from Cos. Antrim and Londonderry, 1830s
  www.ancestryireland.com/family-records/emigrants-from- counties-antrim-and-londonderry-1830s/
  Subscription required

Carlow
- County Carlow Genealogy: Ships Passenger Lists
  www.rootsweb.ancestry.com/~irlcar2/ship_passenger.htm

Cavan
- Cavan Persons in U.S. Records
  http://home.wavecable.com/~colin/genuki/CAV/USRecords.html

Clare
- Donated Material: Emigration Records
  www.clarelibrary.ie/eolas/coclare/genealogy/don_tran/ emigration/index_emigration.htm
  Collection of Clare material from passenger lists, etc.
- Clare Past Forum Emigration List Project 1892-1924
  www.clarelibrary.ie/eolas/coclare/genealogy/emigrants/ emigration_list_project.htm

Donegal
- Passenger Lists - Donegal Emigrants
  http://freepages.genealogy.rootsweb.ancestry.com/~donegal/ passengers.htm
  Various lists of passengers from Donegal to North America, Australia, and New Zealand.
- Assisted Immigrants from Donegal arriving in Lyttleton, New Zealand, 1855-1874
  http://freepages.genealogy.rootsweb.ancestry.com/~donegal/ donpass.htm
- Donegal Relief Fund, Australia
  http://freepages.genealogy.rootsweb.ancestry.com/~donegal/ relief.htm
  Emigrant records of the Donegal Relief Fund, 1858-62.

Galway
- Galway Emigrant Index, 1828-1866
  http://freepages.genealogy.rootsweb.ancestry.com/~maddenps/ GALWAYEM.htm
  Emigrants to Australia.

Kerry
- Lansdowne's Estate in Kenmare Assisted Emigration Plan
  www.rootsweb.ancestry.com/~irlker/lansdowne.html
  www.igp-web.com/Kerry/lansdowne.html
- State-Aided Emigration Scheme: Castlemaine
  www.rootsweb.ancestry.com/~irlker/castlemigr.htm
  www.igp-web.com/Kerry/castlemigr.html

- Ellis Island Records: Immigrants from Castlegregory
  http://www.igp-web.com/Kerry/elliscastab.html

Kilkenny
- Famine Emigration: Castlecomer Area 1847-1853
  www.connorsgenealogy.com/Kilkenny/FamineEmigration.htm
  List of emigrants from Co. Kilkenny.

Limerick
- Kilmallock Workhouse Emigration
  **http://freepages.genealogy.rootsweb.ancestry.com/
  ~mccarthykathryn/kilmallock_workhouse.htm**

Londonderry See also Antrim
- Emigration from Aghadowey Parish, 1834-1835
  www.rootsweb.ancestry.com/~nirldy/aghadowey/ag_osmem.htm

Louth
- Louth, Ireland, Immigration Records
  www.rootsweb.com/~irllou/Immigration
  Various lists of emigrants.

Mayo
- Mayo County Library: Emigrant Letters
  www.mayolibrary.ie/en/LocalStudies/Emigration/
- Emigration from Ballycroy, Co. Mayo, Ireland
  **http://freepages.genealogy.rootsweb.ancestry.com/~deesegenes/
  bballycroy.htm**

Meath
- Meath, Ireland Immigration Records
  www.rootsweb.ancestry.com/~irlmea2/Immigration/index.htm
  Various lists of emigrants.

Roscommon
- Roscommon Emigration Records
  www.igp-web.com/IGPArchives/ire/roscommon/emigration.htm
  From Ballykilcline.

Sligo
- Ships Sailing from Sligo
  www.rootsweb.ancestry.com/~irlsli/shipshesli.html

Tipperary
- Almost Tipperary Emigrant Index
  **http://freepages.genealogy.rootsweb.ancestry.com/~maddenps/
  TIPPEM3.htm**
  Lists those who paid their passage to Australia, but apparently did not go.
- Tipperary Emigrants and their Relatives
  http://freepages.genealogy.rootsweb.ancestry.com/~maddenps
  Links to various databases.

Tyrone
- County Tyrone: Ships
  www.cotyroneireland.com/menus/schools.html
  Collection of ships' passenger lists.

Wexford
- Irish Immigrants From County Wexford: New York Port Arrival Records, 1846-1851
  www.igp-web.com/Wexford/immigrants_wex.htm
- Irish Immigrants from County Wexford: New York Port Arrival Records 1846-1851
  www.rootsweb.ancestry.com/~irlwex2/wexford_immigrants.html

Enclosure Records
- Reports and Returns Relating to Evictions in the Kilrush Union (1847-1849)
  **www.clarelibrary.ie/eolas/coclare/history/kr_evictions/
  kr_union_evictions_1849.htm**
  Numerous pages listing enclosure evictions.

Encumbered Estates
- Encumbered Estates
  www.proni.gov.uk/no.16_-_encumbered_estates__69kb_.pdf
  Brief note on a source giving tenants' names for many mid-19th c. estates throughout Ireland.

- Landed estates court rentals
  www.irish-genealogy-toolkit.com/landed-estates-court-rentals.html
- Landed Estates Court Rentals 1850-1885
  http://search.findmypast.ie/search-world-Records/landed-estates-court-rentals-1850-1885
  Pay per view.
- Ireland, Landed Estate Court Records (FamilySearch Historical Records)
  https://familysearch.org/learn/wiki/en/Ireland,_Landed_Estate_Court_Records_%28FamilySearch_Historical_Records%29

Carlow

- Encumbered Land Sales: Carlow c.1855 & 1860
  www.rootsweb.ancestry.com/~irlcar2/Encumbered_Land_Sales_1855_60.htm

Offaly

- Encumbered Estate property of Garrett O'Moore, Esq., Lots 1-11, 1852
  www.igp-web.com/IGPArchives/ire/offaly/land/enc-est1.txt

Roscommon

- Encumbered Estate property of Garrett O'Moore, Esq., Lots 13-17, (Bellfield, Gortanabla, Togher, Carrowreagh & Carrownure) 1852
  www.igp-web.com/IGPArchives/ire/roscommon/land/enc-est-bellfield.txt
  Continued at /enc-est-glanmore.txt for Cloonbigney, Carrigaharna, Castle Park & Lisbrack, & Glanmore.

Sligo

- Sligo Land Records
  www.igp-web.com/IGPArchives/ire/sligo/land.htm
  Includes various 'encumbered estate transcriptions'.

Tipperary

- Tipperary Encumbered Estates
  www.igp-web.com/tipperary/estates/index.htm

Waterford

- Waterford Ireland genealogy projects: Some Encumbered Estates
  www.igp-web.com/Waterford/land/estndx.htm

Estate Records *see also* Deeds & Encumbered Estates
- Estate Records
  www.irishtimes.com/ancestor/browse/records/land/estate.htm
  Advice page. For lists of estate records for each county, click 'counties', the specific county of interest, & 'estate records'.
- Estate Records
  http://webarchive.nationalarchives.gov.uk/+/
  http://www.movinghere.org.uk/galleries/roots/irish/irishrecords/estaterecords.htm
  Advice page.
- Irish Land Records
  http://globalgenealogy.com/globalgazette/gazkb/gazkb68.htm
  Advice page. Continued at /gazkb670.htm.
- Genealogy Records: Estate Records
  www.nationalarchives.ie/genealogy1/genealogy-records/estate-records
  In the National Archives of Ireland. See also /private-source-records.
- Your Family Tree: 8. Landed Estate Records
  www.proni.gov.uk/no.8_-_landed_estates__74kb_.pdf
  In the Public Record Office of Northern Ireland. For introductions to many individual collections, see
  /index/research_and_records_held/introductions_to_significant_privately_deposited_archives.htm.
- Irish Estate Records
  www.from-ireland.net/irish-estate-records
  Lists records by county.
- Simington, Robert C., ed. *The Civil survey A.D.1654-1656.* 10 vols. Irish Manuscripts Commission, 1931-61
  www.irishmanuscripts.ie/servlet/Controller?action=digitisation_backlist
  Digitised books; click on titles.
- Local History: 9. The Commissioners Church Temporalities In Ireland (FIN/10/10)
  www.proni.gov.uk/no.9_-__church_temporalities__56kb_.pdf
  Discussion of 19th c. estate records of the Church of Ireland.

Antrim
- 1728 Hertford Estate Rent Rolls
  www.ancestryireland.com/family-records/hertford-estate-rent-roll-1728
  Subscription required. Co. Antrim estates.

Armagh
- Gosford Papers (D1606 and D2259)
  www.proni.gov.uk/gosford_papers_summary.pdf

- Tenants Manor of Brownlows-Derry, County Armagh, c.1670-1799
  www.ancestryireland.com/family-records/tenants-manor-of-brownlows-derry-county-armagh-c-1670-1799
  Subscription required.

Carlow
- Index to Surveys
  www.rootsweb.ancestry.com/~irlcar2/Surveys_index.htm
  Various pages relating to estates in Co. Carlow.

Cavan
- Known estate records for Cavan
  www.irishtimes.com/ancestor/fuses/counties/index.cfm?fuseaction=estates&CityCounty=Cavan
- County Cavan Ireland Genweb Project: Estate Records
  https://sites.google.com/site/countycavanirelandgenweb/estate-records
  List.
- Principal Landed Proprietors 1802
  http://home.wavecable.com/~colin/genuki/CAV/Proprietors1802.htm
  List for Co. Cavan.

Clare
- Survey of Estate papers in the National Library of Ireland and the National Archives of Ireland: Co. Clare
  www.clarelibrary.ie/eolas/coclare/genealogy/estate_papers/estate_papers.htm

- Donated Material: Registers, Rent-rolls & other Land Records
  www.clarelibrary.ie/eolas/coclare/genealogy/don_tran/regs/index_regs.htm
  Collection of various Co. Clare estate records.

Connacht
- Connacht and Munster Landed Estates Database
  www.landedestates.ie

Cork
- County Cork: Land and Landholders
  http://freepages.genealogy.rootsweb.ancestry.com/~mturner/cork/a_land.htm
  Links page.
- Bandon Leases and Tenancies 1600s To 1800s
  www.bandon-genealogy.com/Bandon_leases.htm
- Index to Map of the lands of Coolfadda and the Town of Bandon 1717
  www.bandon-genealogy.com/bandon-survey.htm
  Index to the names on an estate map. Further information at
  /bandon-survey-south.htm.

Donegal
- Civil Survey 1654: County Donegal
  www.ulsterancestry.com/ua-free_DonegalCivilSurvey1654.html
- Abercorn Estate: Survey of the Manor of Magavelin & Lismochery, Co Donegal 1781
  http://freepages.genealogy.rootsweb.ancestry.com/~donegal/abercorn1781.htm
- Tenants on the Abercorn Donegal Estate, Laggan Area, Co. Donegal, Ireland, 1794
  http://freepages.genealogy.rootsweb.ancestry.com/~donegal/abercorn.htm
- List of Renters who Signed a 21 yr lease with Abercorn Dec 1789, Mongavelin Estate, Co Donegal
  http://freepages.genealogy.rootsweb.ancestry.com/~donegal/abercornrent.htm

Down
- Annesley Papers
  www.proni.gov.uk/introduction_annesley-3.pdf

Fermanagh
- Rent Rolls, Estates and Misc. Land Records
  www.igp-web.com/Fermanagh/Donated.htm#13
  Miscellaneous Fermanagh files in Excel format.

Kerry
- Kenmare Papers
  www.proni.gov.uk/introduction_kenmare_d4151-2.pdf
  Estate records of the Kenmare family of Killarney, Co. Kerry; the estate covered much of Co. Kerry, and also various places in Co's. Carlow, Clare, Cork, Kilkenny, Laois, Limerick, & Tipperary.

Laois
- Laois Papers: Rentals
  www.familyhistory.ie/docs/archives/Laois%20Papers%20Rentals.pdf

Londonderry
- Introduction: Drapers Company
  www.proni.gov.uk/introduction__drapers__d3632.pdf
- Rent Rolls of the Castlestewart and Lissan Estates from 1786
  www.ancestryireland.com/family-records/rent-rolls-of-the-castlestewart-and-lissan-estates-from-1786
  Subscription required. Estates in Co's Londonderry & Tyrone.
- Rent Rolls circa 1800 various townlands, mostly Tamlaght O'Crilly
  www.torrens.org.uk/Genealogy/BannValley/misc/rentrolls.html
- Skinners' Company estate, County Londonderry, 1886-97
  www.ancestryireland.com/family-records/skinners-index-proni-records
  Lists tenants. Requires subscription.

Louth
- County Louth: Tenants of Lord Roden, circa 1837
  www.rootsweb.ancestry.com/~fianna/county/louth/rodn1837.html

- 1839 Some Tenants of Lord Roden from 'The Roden Title'
  www.jbhall.freeservers.com/1839_roden_tenants.htm
  Mainly Dundalk area, Co. Louth.

Mayo
- 1815 Town of Westport Rent Roll
  http://freepages.genealogy.rootsweb.ancestry.com/~deesegenes/wes.html
- Marquis of Sligo rent roll: Old Head estate, Mayo, 1802
  http://freepages.genealogy.rootsweb.ancestry.com/~deesegenes/rent.html

Munster *See* Connacht

Roscommon
- Strokestown Park: The Irish National Famine Museum: Strokestown Park Archive Papers
  www.strokestownpark.ie/famine-museum/archive-papers
  Estate records of the Famine years.

Sligo
- Sligo County Ireland: Kingston Estate Rental 1926
  www.rootsweb.ancestry.com/~irlsli/kingstonrental1926.html
  Rental at sale of the Earl of Kingston's estate.

Tyrone
- County Tyrone: Estate Records and Papers
  www.cotyroneireland.com/menus/estate.html
  Various pages of transcripts, especially from the Abercorn estate. See also **/rental.htm**
- Bready Ancestry: Abercorn estate records
  www.breadyancestry.com/index.php?id=abercornestate
  atabase of various estate records, 18-19th c.
- Hamilton Rent Books
  www.ulsterancestry.com/ua-free_HamiltonRentBooks.html
  For Strabane, 17-19th c.

Wexford

- Wexford Land Records
  www.igp-web.com/IGPArchives/ire/wexford/land.htm
  Includes rental of the Earl of Portsmouth, 1829, and other estate records.
- Estate Records, County Wexford
  http://freepages.genealogy.rootsweb.ancestry.com/~nyirish/
  Estate%20Records%20County%20Wexford.html
  List of collections in the National Library of Ireland.
- Brooks, Eric St. John, ed. *Knights' fees in County Wexford, Carlow and Kilkenny (13th-15th centuries).* Irish Manuscripts Commission, 1950.
  www.irishmanuscripts.ie/digital/Knights%27%20Fees%
  20Counties%20Wexford%20Carlow%20Kilkenny/

Flax Lists

- Mill work and flax growers in Ireland
  www.irish-genealogy-toolkit.com/spinning-wheel-entitlement.html
  Introduction to the flax lists.
- Irish Flax Growers 1796
  www.failteromhat.com/flax1796.php
  Separate pages for all counties.
- Index to 1796 Flaxgrowers Bounty List
  www.ancestryireland.com/family-records/index-to-1796-
  flaxgrowers-bounty-list
  Subscription required.
- Irish Flax Growers List 1796
  www.ancestry.com/search/db.aspx?dbid=3732
  Pay per view.

Antrim

- Antrim, 1796 Spinning Wheel Index
  www.ajmorris.com/dig/toc/antres.htm
  Scroll down to title. Subscription required.

Armagh

- Flax Grower roster for County Armagh, 1796
  www.igp-web.com/armagh/records/FlaxGrowers.htm
- The Armagh Flax Growers Bounty 1796
  www.lurganancestry.com/flaxlist.htm

Cavan

- 1796 Flax Growers List
  http://freepages.genealogy.rootsweb.ancestry.com/~adrian/
  Cavan.htm
  Scroll down to title. Pages for 29 places in Co. Cavan

Clare

- County Clare: Irish Flax Growers 1796
  www.connorsgenealogy.com/clare/clareflax.htm

Donegal

- The 1796 Spinning Wheel Premium Entitlement List, Co. Donegal
  http://freepages.genealogy.rootsweb.ancestry.com/~donegal/
  flaxlist1.htm
  See also **/flaxlist2.htm**

Down

- Flax Growers of Ireland 1796: County Down
  http://countydown.x10.mx/html/index2.htm

Fermanagh

- Flax Growers List of 1796
  www.rootsweb.ancestry.com/~nirfer2/Documents/Misc_Records/
  Flax_growers_list_1796.doc
  For Co. Fermanagh.

Kerry

- County Kerry: 1796 Flax Seed Premium Entitlement List
  www.rootsweb.ancestry.com/~irlker/flax1796.html
  www.igp-web.com/Kerry/flax1796.html

Limerick

- County Limerick: Irish Flax Growers, 1796
  www.connorsgenealogy.com/LIM/flaxgrowers.htm

Londonderry

- Flax Grower List 1796 for County Derry
  www.igp-web.com/Derry/Old_Derry/Flax_1796.htm

Louth

- 1796 The Flax Growers of County Louth
  www.jbhall.freeservers.com/1796_flax_growers.htm

Monaghan

- Surname Index to the 1796 Flax Seed Premium Entitlement Lists
  http://aharney.us/monaghan/spinning.htm
  For Co. Monaghan.

Sligo

- County of Sligo
  www.rootsweb.ancestry.com/~irlsli/flaxgrowers.html
  Flaxgrowers list, 1796.

Tyrone

- County Tyrone: Spinning Wheel Bounty List (Flax Seed Premiums)
  www.cotyroneireland.com/menus/flax.html

Freeholders Records *See* Electoral Registers & Freeholders Records

Game Licences

- Game Certificates, Monday, October 12th, 1818
  www.rootsweb.ancestry.com/~irlcar2/Game_Certificates.htm
  Co.Carlow.
- Clare Game Licences, from the Clare journal, 1810-1821
  www.celticcousins.net/ireland/cl1810g.htm
- Game Licences: Freeman's journal, 27 & 30 September 1809
  http://members.iinet.net.au/~nickred/lists/Dublin_game_1809.htm
  Issued in Dublin.

Grand Jury Records

- Your Family Tree 19: Grand Jury Records
  www.proni.gov.uk/no.19_-_grand_jury__73kb_.pdf
  List of Public Record Office of Northern Ireland holdings.

Louth

- Louth County Council: Online Digital Archives
  www.louthcoco.ie/en/Services/Archives/Online-Digital-Archives
  Grand Jury query books for Louth, 1786- 1813, 1815-1816, & 1823-1899.

Waterford

- Waterford City & County Council: Grand Jury Collections
  www.waterfordcouncil.ie/en/Resident/Archives/Explore,
  Collections/Grand,Jury,Collection

Griffiths Valuation

- Is There More in Griffith's Valuation Than Just Names
  www.leitrim-roscommon.com/GRIFFITH/more_to_griffiths.html
- Richard Griffith's Valuation – a mid-19th century gem
  www.irish-genealogy-toolkit.com/Griffiths-Valuation.html
- Griffith's Primary Valuation Records: Search
  www.from-ireland.net/griffiths-primary-valuation
- Griffith's Valuation Online
  www.irishtimes.com/ancestor/browse/records/land/grvaonline.htm
  General discussion of three separate databases.
- Griffiths Valuation: a 19th century Irish census substitute
  http://familytreemaker.genealogy.com/30_griff.html
  Introduction.
- Your Family Tree 20: How to Use Griffiths Valuation
  www.proni.gov.uk/no.20_-_griffiths_valuation__72kb_.pdf
  From the Public Record Office of Northern Ireland.
- The Ireland List Griffiths Valuation Page
  http://freepages.genealogy.rootsweb.ancestry.com/~irelandlist/
  anc.html
- An Explanation of Griffith's Valuation
  www.rootsweb.ancestry.com/~irlker/griffexp.html
- Griffith's Valuation
  www.irishtimes.com/ancestor/browse/records/land/grva.htm

Databases

- Griffiths Valuation
  www.askaboutireland.ie/griffith-valuation/index.xml
- Griffith's Valuation 1847-1864
  http://search.findmypast.ie/search-world-Records/griffiths-
  valuation-1847-1864

  Pay per view database.

- Ireland, Griffith's Valuation, 1847-1864
  http://search.ancestry.co.uk/search/db.aspx?dbid=1269
  Pay per view.
- Griffiths Valuation 1848-1864
  www.failteromhat.com/griffiths.php
  Pages for every county.

Antrim
- Ireland Householders Index, County Antrim
  search.ancestry.co.uk/search/db.aspx?dbid=4631
  Index to Griffith's Valuation, and to the tithe applotment books

Carlow
- Griffith's Valuation of Ireland, 1848-1864 … The Valuation for Carlow County was taken c.1844: Baronies, Parishes & Townlands in the County of Carlow.
  www.rootsweb.ancestry.com/~irlcar2/valuations.htm
  Transcript.

Clare
- Griffiths Valuation 1852/1855: County Clare Surname Index
  www.clarelibrary.ie/eolas/coclare/genealogy/census_search_forms/index.htm

Cork
- County Cork: Griffiths Valuation of Ireland, 1848-1864
  http://freepages.genealogy.rootsweb.ancestry.com/~mturner/cork/a_griffith.htm
  Gateway to pages of transcripts and indexes.
- Ginni Swanton's Web Site: Griffiths Valuation Details
  www.ginnisw.com/griffith's%20Valuation%20Details.htm
  Scanned records for various Co. Cork parishes.

Donegal
- 1857 Griffiths Valuation of Co. Donegal
  http://freepages.genealogy.rootsweb.ancestry.com/~donegal/griffiths.htm
  Includes indexes for each parish.

- Beagh Parish Griffiths Valuation in 1850's: Heads of Households
  www.celticcousins.net/ireland/griffith.htm
- 1857 Griffith's Valuation: Derrynacarrow East, or Bellanaboy - Stranasaggart - Commeen, Donegal, Ireland
  www.reocities.com/Heartland/Estates/6587/Grif1857.html
- Griffiths Valuation for Inishkeeragh, no.359; Cloghcor; Fallagowan; Gortgarra
  http://freepages.genealogy.rootsweb.ancestry.com/~donegaleire/Dongrifinish.html
- Griffiths Valuation for Templecrone Parish 1857
  http://freepages.genealogy.rootsweb.ancestry.com/~donegaleire/Dongrifinish2.html

  Continued in **/Dongrifinish3.html**

Down
- Griffith's Valuation Index: County Down, 1863-64
  http://countydown.x10.mx/html/index2.htm
- Griffith Valuation: Lawrencetown 1857
  http://lawrencetown.com/history/griffith.htm

Kerry
- Griffiths Valuations: County Kerry
  www.igp-web.com/Kerry/griffith.html
- County Kerry: Griffiths Valuations
  www.rootsweb.ancestry.com/~irlker/griffith.html
- Family History Library Film Numbers for (Griffiths) Valuations for Kerry County
  www.rootsweb.ancestry.com/~irlker/griffilm.html
- Griffiths Valuations
  www.rootsweb.ancestry.com/~irlker/griffith.html
  For selected Co. Kerry parishes.

Kilkenny
- Griffith's Valuation Index: by last name: County Kilkenny, Ireland (circa 1849-1850)
  www.rootsweb.ancestry.com/~irlkik/griffiths/index.htm

Leitrim

- Leitrim-Roscommon Griffiths Database
  www.leitrim-roscommon.com/GRIFFITH
- County Leitrim Records: Griffiths Valuation
  www.irelandgenweb.com/irllet/records.htm
  Scroll down for indexes to the civil parishes of Annaduff, Carrigallen, Cloone, Cloonlogher. Drumlease, Drumreilly, Inishmagrath, Killarga Mohill, & Oughterragh.

Limerick

- Griffith's Valuation of Limerick City, 1850
  www.limerickcity.ie/Library/LocalStudies/GriffithsValuationof LimerickCity1850

Longford

- Griffiths Valuation [Cancelled Books] (1860+)
  www.igp-web.com/Longford/valuations1.htm

Mayo

- Griffith's Valuation for County Mayo
  www.ajmorris.com/dig/toc/mygrif.htm
  For index, see /_01mydx.htm
  Pay per view.
- Griffith Valuation for Co. Mayo
  http://freepages.genealogy.rootsweb.ancestry.com/ ~deesegenes/grif.html
  For a few parishes only.
- Griffith's Valuation in the Union of Westport
  www.bernieworld.net/Griffiths/WptG.htm

Roscommon *See* Leitrim

Sligo

- Sligo Griffiths Valuation Records, 1858
  www.rootsweb.ancestry.com/~irlsli/griffithsopen.html
  Covers Kilcoman, Kilfree, & Lislary only.

Tipperary

- Griffith's Valuation
  www.irelandgenweb.com/irltip/records.htm
  Scroll down for indexes to the valuation for Tipperary parishes.
- County Tipperary Surname Index
  www.connorsgenealogy.com/tipp/SurnameIndex.htm
  Index to Griffiths Valuation and the Tithe Applotment Books. Also
  www.connorsgenealogy.com/tipp
  Scroll down for local valuations.

Tyrone

- County Tyrone: Griffiths Valuation
  www.cotyroneireland.com/menus/griffiths.html
  Includes transcripts for various parishes and townlands.

Waterford

- The Family Names of Rathgormack - Clonea
  www.rathgormack.com/names.htm
  Includes Index to Griffith's Valuation for Co.Waterford.

Wicklow

- Full Name Index to Householders for Griffiths Primary Valuation, County Wicklow, Ireland
  www.ajmorris.com/dig/toc/_01wkgi.htm
  Pay per view.
- Griffiths Primary Valuation of Rateable Property for County Wicklow: Naas Poor Law Union
  www.ajmorris.com/dig/toc/_01wkns.htm
  Pay per view. For Rathdown Poor Law Union, see /_01wkrd.htm

Gun Licences

- Gun Licences 1832-1836: Names of persons in Carlow, Ireland to whom a licence for arms has been granted
  www.rootsweb.ancestry.com/~irlcar2/Gun_Licences.htm

Hearth Tax

Armagh

- Hearth Money Roll, Armagh 1665
  www.failteromhat.com/armaghhearth.php

- Lurgan Hearth Tax Rolls, 1664
  www.lurganancestry.com/hearthtax.htm

Donegal
- County Donegal, Ireland
  www.reocities.com/Heartland/Estates/6587/Donegal.html
  Includes various hearth tax lists.
- Online Land Records for County Donegal
  http://freepages.genealogy.rootsweb.ancestry.com/~donegal/
                                                              land.htm
  Includes various hearth money rolls, 1665.
- Donegal Hearth Money Rolls
  www.ulsterancestry.com/ShowFreePage.php?id=227
  For Leck, see **/HearthMoneyRoll-1665_Leck.html**

Louth
- Hearth Money Roll, Louth, 1664
  www.failteromhat.com/louthhearth.php
- Hearth Money Roll Dundalk 1663
  www.ulsterancestry.com/ShowFreePage.php?id=311

Monaghan
- Hearth Money Roll: Monaghan 1663-1665
  www.failteromhat.com/monaghanhearth.php

Sligo
- Hearth Money Roll, Sligo 1665
  www.failteromhat.com/sligohearth.php

Tipperary
- 1664 Hearth Money Rolls for the Baronies of Ida and Offa, Co. Tipperary
  http//freepages.genealogy.rootsweb.ancestry.com/~irish/
                                                  Tipperary/1664iffa.htm

Tyrone
- County Tyrone: Hearth Money Rolls
  www.cotyroneireland.com/menus/hearth.html
  Includes transcripts for various parishes.

Wicklow
- Arklow Hearth Money Rolls, Co. Wicklow, 1669
  www.from-ireland.net/arklow-hearth-money-rolls-1669

Hospital Records
- Hospital records in the National Archives of Ireland
  www.nationalarchives.ie/topics/Medical_sources/Hospital_
                                                              records.pdf

Justiciary Rolls
- Calendar of the Justiciary Rolls, Ireland, Volume 1
  www.worldvitalrecords.com/indexinfo.aspx?ix=ia_
                                          calendarofjustic01irel
  Pay per view. From printed books.

Land Grants
- The Cromwellian Settlement
  www.clarelibrary.ie/eolas/coclare/history/cromwell_settlement.htm
  Introduction to mid-seventeenth century land grants.
- Names of the Cromwellian Adventurers for land in Ireland
  www.ulsterancestry.com/ShowFreePage.php?id=132
  In 1642-6; surnames of those entitled to land grants.
- Books of Survey and Distribution
  http://en.wikipedia.org/wiki/Books_of_survey_and_distribution
  Introduction; these books list those granted lands, late 17th c.
- Local History: 4. The Books of Survey and Distribution
  www.proni.gov.uk/no.4_-_the_books_of_survey_and_distribution
                                                              __48kb_.pdf
  Names of landowners in Northern Ireland, c.1680.

Cavan
- Plantation of County Cavan
  http://home.wavecable.com/~colin/genuki/CAV/Plantation.html
  List of land grantees, 1612-13.

Clare See Roscommon

Donegal
- Some of the Earliest Settlers in the Laggan Area of Co. Donegal, Ireland
  http://homepages.rootsweb.ancestry.com/~mwi/laggan.txt
  Early 17th c.

- Captain Nicholas Pynnar's Survey 1618 A.D. of the Land Grants Given in 1608, Barony of Raphoe
  www.finnvalley.ie/history/welshtown/pynnar.htm

Galway See Roscommon

Kerry
- County Kerry: Extract from Books of Survey and Distribution (1680): Aghadoe - Kilcummin - Killarney – Killaha
  www.rootsweb.ancestry.com/~irlker/survey1680.html

Kilkenny See Tipperary

Mayo See Roscommon

Roscommon
- Simington, Robert C., ed. *Book of survey and distribution, vol.1. County of Roscommon.* Irish Manuscripts Commission, 1949.
  www.irishmanuscripts.ie/digital/surveydistributionv1/index.html
  Digitised book. Further volumes cover May (vol.2), Galway (vol.3), and Clare (vol.4)

Tipperary
- Curtis, Edmund, ed. Calendar of Ormonde Deeds 1172-1350. Irish Manuscripts Commission, 1932.
  www.irishmanuscripts.ie/digital/Calendar%20of%20Ormond%20Deeds%20Vol.%20I.%201172-1350/
  Covers (mainly) Co's. Tipperary and Kilkenny. Five further vols cover up to 1603. See also
  www.from-ireland.net/ormond-deeds1-kilkenny, & **-deeds2-** etc for Kilkenny.

Ulster
- The Scottish Undertakers
  www.rootsweb.ancestry.com/~nirfer/undertakers.htm
  List of Scottish applicants for land grants in Ulster, 1689

Landowners' Census
- Land Owners in Ireland 1876
  www.failteromhat.com/lo1876.php
  Digitised images of the original returns for all counties (these are in alphabetical order). Also available pay per view on a number of sites:
  http://search.ancestry.co.uk/search/db.aspx?dbid=48475
  www.ajmorris.com/dig/toc/_01irlo.htm
  www.familyrelatives.com/search/search_landrecords.php?
  search=Ireland
- Ireland Genealogical Projects
  http://www.igp-web.com/IGPArchives/
  Use search box at foot of page to search 'landowners'. Pages for most counties.

Armagh
- Armagh Land Owners 1870-1879
  www.lurganancestry.com/lurgantown1870-79.htm
- Landowners in Co. Armagh circa 1870's
  www.rootsweb.ancestry.com/~nirarm/landowners.html
- Armagh Landowners List, 1876
  http://freepages.genealogy.rootsweb.ancestry.com/
  ~donaghmore1/armagh/arldownlst.html

Carlow
- Carlow Landowners 1871
  www.rootsweb.ancestry.com/~irlcar2/Carlow_1871.htm

Cavan
- 1876 Land Owners
  http://home.wavecable.com/~colin/genuki/CAV/1876Land.html

Clare
- Land Owners in Clare: return of owners of land of one acre and upwards in County Clare, 1876
  www.clarelibrary.ie/eolas/coclare/genealogy/
  land_owners_in_clare.htm

Cork
- Land Owners in Ireland 1876: Return of Owners of Land of One Acre and Upwards in County Cork
www.ginnisw.com/Cork%20Landowners%201876/Thumb/
Thumbs1.htm

Donegal
- 1876 Landowners Donegal
www.ulsterancestry.com/1876_Landowners_Co-Donegal.html

- 1876 Landowners, Co. Donegal
http://freepages.genealogy.rootsweb.ancestry.com/~donegal/
1876land.htm

Down
- List of County Down Land Deeds in 1876
http://countydown.x10.mx/html/deed_letters/main.htm
From the Parliamentary returns; nothing to do with deeds, despite the title.

Fermanagh
- [Fermanagh Landowners 1876]
www.rootsweb.com/~nirfer2/Documents/Misc_Records/
1876_Landowners_Fermanagh.xls

Galway
- Landowners in Co. Galway, circa 1870s
www.genealogy.com/users/c/e/l/Nancy-R-Celleri/FILE/
0005page.html

- Landowners in Co. Galway, circa 1870's
www.rootsweb.ancestry.com/~irlgal/landowner_records.htm

Kilkenny
- Landowners in 1876, County Kilkenny, Ireland
www.rootsweb.ancestry.com/~irlkik/records/1876land.htm

Limerick
- Owners of Land of One Acre and Upwards in the County of Limerick, 1876
www.limerickcity.ie/Library/LocalStudies/
OwnersofLandofOneAcreandUpwardsintheCountyofLimerick1876

Roscommon
- Landowners of Roscommon County in 1871
www.rootsweb.ancestry.com/~irlros/returnof.htm~

Sligo
- Land Owners in Co. Sligo, late 1870's
www.rootsweb.ancestry.com/~irlsli/landowners.html

Westmeath
- Landowners in Co. Westmeath, circa 1870's
www.rootsweb.ancestry.com/~irlwem/Landowners.html

Wicklow
- Clever Cat Genealogy Data
http://ccg.haldac.info/CCGdata.html
Mainly 'landowners in Wicklow 1876'.

Marriage Licence Bonds

Armagh See also Cavan & Tyrone

Cavan See also Tyrone
- Church of Ireland. Marriage Licence Bonds. Diocese of Kilmore & Ardagh
freepages.genealogy.rootsweb.ancestry.com/~adrian/ColKilm.htm
For 1697-1844. Covers parts of Cos. Armagh, Cavan, Leitrim, Monaghan, Sligo, etc., 18-19th c.

Clare
- Killaloe, Co. Clare Marriage License Bonds, 1680-1720 and 1760-1762
www.celticcousins.net/ireland/killaloe.htm
Also available at
www.the-e-site.com/irish/CLARE/Marriages/killaloe.html

Cork

- Gillman's Index to Marriage Licence Bonds: Cork and Ross
  **www.corkpastandpresent.ie/genealogy/
  gillmansindextomarriagelicencebonds-corkandross/**
  Digitised edition of Gillman, Herbert Webb. *Index to the marriage licence
  bonds of the Diocese of Cloyne and Ross, Ireland, for the years from
  1623 to 1750.* Guy & Co., 1896-7. Also available (pay per view) at
  **www.worldvitalrecords.com/indexinfo.aspx?ix=
  ia_indextomarriagel00cork**
- Green's Index to Marriage Licence Bonds: Cloyne
  **www.corkpastandpresent.ie/genealogy/
  greensindextomarriagelicencebonds-cloyne/**
  Digitised edition of Green, T. George H. *Index to the marriage licence
  bonds of the Diocese of Cloyne, for the years from 1630 to 1800.* Guy &
  Co., 1899-1900. Also available (pay per view) at
  **www.findmypast.ie/articles/world-records/full-list-of-the-irish-
  family-history-records/life-events-birth-marriage-death/marriage-
  licence-bonds-diocese-of-cloyne-1630-1800.**

Donegal

- Find your ancestors in Raphoe Marriage Bonds 1710-55, 1817-30
  **www.findmypast.ie/articles/world-records/full-list-of-the-irish-
  family-history-records/life-events-birth-marriage-death/raphoe-
  marriage-bonds-1710-55-and-1817-30**
  Pay per view.

Fermanagh *See* Tyrone

Galway

- Find your ancestors in Clonfert Marriage Licence Bonds
  **www.findmypast.ie/articles/world-records/full-list-of-the-irish-
  family-history-records/life-events-birth-marriage-death/
  clonfert-marriage-bonds-1663-1857**

Laois

- Laois, Dublin Prerogative Marriage Licenses
  **www.igp-web.com/IGPArchives/ire/laois/churches/
  dub-marriage-bonds.txt**

- Laois Marriage Bonds from the Dioceses of Ferns, Ossory & Leighlin,
  A-D
  **www.the-e-site.com/irish/LAOIS/Marriages/
  laois-marriage-bonds-from-the-dioceses-of-ferns.htm**

Leitrim *See* Cavan

Monaghan *See* Cavan & Tyrone

Sligo *See* Cavan

Tipperary

- Tipperary Marriage Records
  www.igp-web.com/tipperary/marriages/index.htm
  Includes Church of Ireland marriage licences from Diocese of Dublin
  (Tipperary names) 1638-1794, Diocese of Killaloe marriage licence
  bonds 1680-1762 (Tipperary names), list of dispensations for marriage
  for the year 1859 for the Diocese of Cashel and Emly, & marriage
  licences from the Dioceses of Ossory, Ferns & Leighlin.

Tyrone

- Church of Ireland Marriage Licence Bonds. Diocese of Clogher
  **http://freepages.genealogy.rootsweb.ancestry.com/~adrian/
  ColClog.htm**
  For 1709-1866. The Diocese covers Cos. Tyrone & Fermanagh, with
  parts of Armagh, Cavan & Monaghan.
- Church of Ireland Marriage Licence Bonds: Diocese of Clogher Extracts
  **www.ulsterancestry.com/Church_of_Ireland_MLB_Diocese-
  Clogher.htm**
  18-19th c.

Waterford

- Waterford County Ireland Archives Church Records...Dublin Prerogative
  Marriage Licenses (also called Marriage Bonds)
  **www.igp-web.com/IGPArchives/ire/waterford/churches/
  dub-bonds-wat.txt**

- Marriage Licenses from The Dioceses Of Ossory, Ferns & Leighlin
**www.igp-web.com/IGPArchives/ire/waterford/churches/
mar-ossory-ferns-leighlin.txt**
From Co. Waterford.

Westmeath
- Westmeath Ireland Genealogy: Church of Ireland Marriage Licenses from Diocese of Dublin 1680 -1764
www.igp-web.com/westmeath/groom.htm

Wicklow
- Dublin Diocesan Marriage Licences: 1789-1794
www.igp-web.com/IGPArchives/ire/wicklow/churches/wicklic.txt

Medals
- The Victoria Cross: Britain's Highest Award For Gallantry
www.victoriacross.org.uk/vcross.htm
Scroll down for Irish recipients.

Methodist Records
- Methodist Historical Society of Ireland
http://methodisthistoryireland.org
Includes index of Methodist ministers, & of 'Irish Methodist Churches, Chapels and Preaching Houses'; also historical notes on every church, & a page on 'family history & genealogy'.

Municipal Records

Antrim
- Town Book of the Corporation of Belfast, 1613-1816
**www.worldvitalrecords.com/
indexinfo.aspx?ix=ia_immigrationofiri00myer**
Pay per view.

Armagh
- City of Armagh Householders, 1836-37
**www.ancestryireland.com/family-records/
city-of-armagh-householders-1836-37**

Cork
- Council Book of the Corporation of the City of Cork, From 1609 To 1643, And From 1690 To 1800 (1876)
**www.worldvitalrecords.com/indexinfo.aspx?ix=ia_
councilbookofcor01cork**
Pay per view. Also see
/indexinfo.aspx?ix=ia_councilbookofcor02cork

Dublin
- Dublin Assembly Rolls
www.from-ireland.net/dublin-assembly-rolls-index
For 1716-18, 1731, & 1740-42.

Limerick
- List of the Mayors and Sheriffs of the City of Limerick 1197-1700
www.celticcousins.net/ireland/mayors.htm

Londonderry
- Londonderry Corporation Records
**www.proni.gov.uk/index/search_the_archives/
corporationarchive-3.htm**
Includes digitised minute books, 1673-1901.

Louth
- Name Index to Gogarty's Council Book of the Corporation of Drogheda, 1649 – 1734
www.jbhall.freeservers.com/1649-1734_drogheda_corporation.htm
Continued for 1734-1758 at **/1734-1758_drogheda_corporation.htm**.
- The Mayors of Drogheda, 1285-1932
www.jbhall.freeservers.com/1285-1932_drogheda_mayors.htm
- 1692-1841 Dundalk Corporate Officers (Bailiff, Deputy Bailiff & Recorder)
www.jbhall.freeservers.com/1692-1841_dlk_corporate_officers.htm

Motor Vehicle Licences
- Owners of Limerick-registered motor vehicles, 1912-1914
**www.limerickcity.ie/Library/LocalStudies/OwnersofLimerick-
registeredmotorvehicles1912-1914**

Muster Rolls

- Your Family Tree: 12. Militia, Yeomanry Lists, and Muster Rolls
  **www.proni.gov.uk/no.12_-
  _militia__yeomanry___muster_rolls__75kb_.pdf**
  Advice page from the Public Record Office of Northern Ireland

Armagh

- Armagh Muster Rolls c.1630
  www.from-ireland.net/armagh-muster-rolls-1630

Cavan

- 1630 Muster Roll, Co. Cavan
  **http://freepages.genealogy.rootsweb.ancestry.com/~adrian/
  Must1630.htm**

Donegal

- The Muster Roll of the County of Donnagall 1630 A.D., as printed in the Donegal Annual
  www.ulsterancestry.com/ua-free-Muster_Rolls_Donegal_1631.html
- Muster List, Inishowen, Co. Donegal, 1630
  www.from-ireland.net/muster-list-inishowen-donegal-1630/

Fermanagh

- Muster Rolls
  www.igp-web.com/Fermanagh/Donated.htm#5
  Indexes for Co Fermanagh, 1630; in Excel format.
- Fermanagh Muster Rolls, 1630
  www.from-ireland.net/fermanagh-muster-rolls-1630
- From the Muster Roll of the County of Fermanagh 1631
  www.ulsterancestry.com/muster-roll_1663.html
  www.rootsweb.ancestry.com/~nirfer/1631_musterroll.htm

Kilkenny

- Muster List, Kilkenny City, 1667
  www.from-ireland.net/history-muster-kilkenny-1667-ireland
  Further pages cover 1685 **/history-muster-kilkenny-1685-ireland** &
  1690 **/history-muster-kilkenny-1690.**

Londonderry

- County Derry 1631 Muster Roll
  www.rootsweb.ancestry.com/~fianna/county/derry/ldy-1631.html
- 1761 Militia List, Ireland
  www.torrens.org.uk/Genealogy/BannValley/misc/Militia.html
  Londonderry portion.

- Muster Roll on the Ironmongers Estate, Co. Londonderry, Ireland, (circa 1630)
  www.ulsterancestry.com/ShowFreePage.php?id=373

Louth

- 1804 Drogheda Militiamen
  www.jbhall.freeservers.com/drogheda_militiamen.htm
  Also includes Louth Militia 1756, Louth Militia Balloted Men 1804, Louth Militia Recruits 1806, Louth Militia officers 1808, Recruits of the Louth Rifles 1855, etc.

Sligo

- The Sligo regiment of Militia or 22nd
  www.igp-web.com/Sligo/Military/1802_Sligo_Militia.htm
  List for 1802? For 1803, see **/Sligo_Militia_1803.htm**
- Pensions 1796 to 1829
  www.igp-eb.com/Sligo/Military/1796_Military_Pension_Records.htm

Tyrone

- County Tyrone: Muster Rolls and Military
  www.cotyroneireland.com/menus/muster.html

Newspapers *See also* Chapter 8 for announcements
- Ireland Newspapers
  https://familysearch.org/learn/wiki/en/Ireland_Newspapers
- Using historical Irish newspapers for genealogy research
  www.irish-genealogy-toolkit.com/historical-irish-newspapers.html
- Making the Most of Newspapers
  http://www.rootsweb.ancestry.com/~fianna/guide/newsppr.html

- Newspapers
  www.irishtimes.com/ancestor/browse/records/news/
  index2.htm#Newspapers
  Introduction.
- National Library of Ireland: Newspapers
  www.nli.ie/en/family-history-newspapers.aspx
  Includes catalogue of National Library holdings.
- Newspapers available on Microfilm
  www.proni.gov.uk/newspapers_on_microfilm.pdf
  At the Public Record Office of Northern Ireland

Databases & Indexes

- Irish Newspaper Archive
  www.irishnewsarchive.com
- Ireland, Newspapers, 1763-1890
  http://search.ancestry.co.uk/search/db.aspx?dbid=50008
  Pay per view. Digitised images of 30+ newspapers.
- Irish Newspaper Collection
  www.findmypast.ie/articles/world-records/full-list-of-the-irish-
  family-history-records/irish-newspaper-collection
  Digitised Irish newspapers. Pay per view.
- Irish Times Digital Archive, 1859-2010
  www.irishtimes.com/archive
- Ireland Old News
  www.irelandoldnews.com/index.html
  Transcripts of miscellaneous newspaper articles. Includes pages for most counties, 18-20th c.
- Nick Reddan's Newspaper Abstracts
  members.webone.com.au/~nickred/newspaper
  Covers 1750-1840.
- Obituaries of the Irish Diaspora
  www.familyhistory.ie/docs/archives/Obituaries%20for%20website.pdf
  Index to newspaper cuttings, mainly from Canada, some from USA.

Antrim

- Belfast, Northern Ireland, *The Belfast Newsletter,* 1738-1925
  http://search.ancestry.co.uk/search/db.aspx?dbid=2193
  Pay per view digitised images.

- *The Belfast Newsletter index* 1737-1800
  www.ucs.louisiana.edu/bnl

Armagh

- Dave Jassie's County Armagh Research Material Index: Newspapers and Notices
  http://freepages.genealogy.rootsweb.ancestry.com/~jassie/armagh/
  Newspapers

Clare

- Clare Newspaper Records
  www.igp-web.com/IGPArchives/ire/clare/news.htm
- Index to Biographical Notices in the *Clare Champion* newspaper 1935-1985
  www.clarelibrary.ie/eolas/coclare/genealogy/estate_papers/
  estate_papers.htm

Leitrim

- Leitrim Newspaper Index
  http://comres.leitrimcoco.ie/

Tipperary

- Tipperary Newspaper Records
  www.igp-web.com/IGPArchives/ire/tipperary/news.htm

Waterford

- Waterford City & County Libraries: Local Studies: Newspapers
  www.main.cls?surl=Research#contentitem=99dd77ae-
  30b4-431e-9f3c-b1af6e5532b1^1
  For the libraries' World War I & II newspaper archive, see
  /wararchive/searcharticles.aspx.

Outrage Reports

- Research Help: Outrage or Police Reports
  www.from-ireland.net/research-help-outrage-or-police-reports

Papal Army Subscribers

- Subscribers to Clare Papal Army, 1860
  www.clarelibrary.ie/eolas/coclare/genealogy/papal_army_1860.htm
  From Co Clare.

Papal Registers
- Calendar of Entries in the Papal Registers Relating To Great Britain And Ireland. Papal Letters, Volume 1, 1198–1304
  **www.worldvitalrecords.com/indexinfo.aspx?ix=ia_
  calendarofentrie11grea**
  Pay per view. From a printed book.

Parliamentary Papers
- Enhanced British Parliamentary Papers on Ireland 1801-1922
  www.dippam.ac.uk/eppi/Database

Pension Claims
- Ireland Genealogy
  www.ireland-genealogy.com
  Database of pension claims based on extracts from the 1841 & 1851 censuses, for Northern Ireland.
- Old Age Pension - Proof of Age Extraction Claim Forms 1841, 1851
  **www.ancestryireland.com/family-records/old-age-pension-
  proof-of-age-extraction-claim-forms-1841-1851**
  Subscription required.
- Ireland, 1841 and 1851 Census Search Forms
  https://familysearch.org/search/collection/2346275
  Database of claim forms for the Old Age Pension.

Clare
- Census Search Forms, 1841 & 1851
  **www.clarelibrary.ie/eolas/coclare/genealogy/
  census_search_forms/index.htm**
  For Co. Clare.

Donegal
- 1841/1851 Census Search Forms - Templecrone Parish, Co Donegal
  **http://freepages.genealogy.rootsweb.ancestry.com/~donegal/
  dungloeoap.htm**

Tyrone
- Bready Ancestry: Old Age Pension Claims
  www.breadyancestry.com/index.php?id=miscellaneous
  Database for the parishes of Donagheady & Leckpatrick.

- Old Age Pension Claims, Barony of Dungannon 1841-1851
  www.cotyroneireland.com/misc/oap-dungannon.html

Petitions & Other Miscellaneous Name Lists
- Hearts of Steel Memorials, c.1770
  **www.ancestryireland.com/family-records/
  hearts-of-steel-memorials-c-177(**
  Subscription required. Over 1,000 signatures.
- Act of Union Petitions, 1799-1800
  **www.ancestryireland.com/family-records/act-of-union-petitions-
  1799-180(**
  Subscription required.
- Ireland, Lord Viscount Morpeth's Testimonial Roll, 1841
  http://search.ancestry.co.uk/search/db.aspx?dbid=2514
  Pay per view.
- Find your ancestors in The William Smith O'Brien Petition 1848-49
  **www.findmypast.com/articles/world-records/full-list-of-the-irish-
  family-history-records/military-service-and-conflict
  william-smith-obrien-petition-184(**
  Petition against a death sentence listing 80,000 names. Pay per view.
- William Smith O'Brien Petition
  **http://www.worldvitalrecords.com/indexinfo.aspx?ix=eneclann_
  enec00(**
  Pay per view.
- Names regarding Tenant-Right in County Monaghan from Freeman's Journal
  **www.ancestryireland.com/family-records/names-regarding-
  tenant-right-in-county-monaghan-from-freemans-journa(**
  Subscription required.

Clare
- Clare Men in Favour of Union of Britain and Ireland 1799
  www.celticcousins.net/ireland/1799cl.htm
  Declaration from the *Ennis Chronicle*.

Donegal

Donegal Supporters of the Act of Union 1800, compiled from advertisements in the *Belfast Newsletter* between 31 Dec 1799 and 17 Jan 1800
http://freepages.genealogy.rootsweb.ancestry.com/~donegal/ActOfUnion1800a.htm

Kerry

1916 Petition to split Knocknagoshel from the Diocese of Brosna
www.rootsweb.ancestry.com/~irlker/parishpet.html~

Plea Rolls

• The Medieval Irish Plea Rolls: an introduction
www.nationalarchives.ie/topics/Medieval_plea_rolls/Medieval_plea_rolls.pdf

Pollbooks *See* Electoral Registers, Pollbooks, & Freeholders' Records

Poll Tax

Donegal

• County Donegal Surname on the Census, 1659, Poll Money Ordinances
www.reocities.com/Heartland/Estates/6587/Doncensus.html

Kilkenny

• County Kilkenny Down Survey, 1659
www.rootsweb.ancestry.com/~irlkik2/surnames_1659.htm
Discussion, with a list of surnames.

Tipperary

• Tipperary Poll Books
www.igp-web.com/tipperary/polls/index.htm
Actually, not a pollbook, but a poll tax return of 1660.

Poor Law

• Guide to the records of the Poor Law
www.nationalarchives.ie/research/research-guides-and-articles/guide-to-the-records-of-the-poor-law
From the National Archives of Ireland.

• Poor Law Records
www.proni.gov.uk/your_family_tree_series_-_13_-_poor_law_records.pdf
In the Public Record Office of Northern Ireland.
• Frequently Asked Questions. Workhouse Records
www.proni.gov.uk/no.13_-_poor_law_records__40kb.pdf
• Ireland Poorhouses, Poor Law, etc.
https://familysearch.org/learn/wiki/en/Ireland_Poorhouses,_Poor_Law,_Etc
• The Workhouse in Ireland
www.workhouses.org.uk/Ireland
Includes page for each union, listing records (click on 'union lists' at bottom of page)
• Workhouses In Ireland
www.irishfamilyresearch.co.uk/essentialresource8.htm
Introductory guidance.
• Workhouses
www.rootsweb.ancestry.com/~fianna/guide/PLUwork.html
List of Irish records.
• Alphabetical List of Workhouses In Ireland (by county), with Contact Details for Records & Further Information
www.irishfamilyresearch.co.uk/workhouselist.htm
• Poor From England to Ireland, Dec. 1860-Dec. 1862
www.rootsweb.ancestry.com/~ote/ships/irishpoor1860-62.htm
• Some Poor Removals from England to Ireland Jan 1867- Dec. 1869
www.igp-web.com/IGPArchives/ire/countrywide/xmisc/poor-removals02.txt
Lists paupers removed to Ireland, mostly from Liverpool.

Clare

• A Guide to Ennistymon Union, 1839 – 1850
www.clarelibrary.ie/eolas/coclare/history/etworkhouse.htm
For minute books, see also /et_minutes/ennistymon_minutes.htm
• Deaths and Staff in Kilrush and Ennistymon Workhouses 1850-51
www.clarelibrary.ie/eolas/coclare/history/kr_et_workhouses/kr_et_workhouses.htm
• Kilrush Union Minute Books 1849
http://www.clarelibrary.ie/eolas/coclare/history/etworkhouse.htm

Donegal
- Templecrone Parish People Admitted to the Glenties Workhouse in 1851
  http://freepages.genealogy.rootsweb.ancestry.com/~donegal/
  1851gworkhsetemp.htm

Fermanagh
- Workhouse Indexes [Co. Fermanagh]
  www.igp-web.com/Fermanagh/Donated.htm#1
  From Enniskillen & Lowtherston, etc., mostly 1840s. In Excel format.
  See also **#21**

Kerry
- An Gorta Mor: The Great Hunger
  www.thegreathunger.org
  Includes digitised images of Guardian's minute books for Killarney,
  1845-8, etc.

Waterford
- Workhouses/Board of Guardians Collection
  www.waterfordcouncil.ie/en/Resident/Archives/
  Explore,Collections/WorkhousesBoard,of,Guardians,Collection

Presbyterian Records
- Presbyterian Church of Ireland: Church Records
  www.presbyterianireland.org/About-Us/Historical-Information/
  Church-Records
- Presbyterian Historical Society of Ireland
  www.presbyterianhistoryireland.com
  Includes details of an off-line database of Presbyterian ministers.

Quaker Records
- Goodbody, Olive C., ed. *Guide to Irish Quaker records*. Irish
  Manuscripts Commission, 1967.
  www.irishmanuscripts.ie/digital/guidetoirishquakerrecords/
  index.html
  Digitised book.
- Quakers in Ireland: Historical Library
  http://quakers-in-ireland.ie/historical-library

Armagh
- List of subscribers to the Lurgan Quaker Church
  www.lurganancestry.com/quakers1696.htm
  In 1696.

Rates
- Rate Books for the Rural District of Scariff, 1921 & 1926
  www.clarelibrary.ie/eolas/coclare/genealogy/scariff_rate_books_
  1921_1926/rate_books_scariff_1921_1926.htm

Tipperary
- Lackagh Rate Book December 1850
  www.tipperarylibraries.ie/tipperary-studies
  Scroll down; digitised copy.
- Rate for the relief of the poor of Thurles & Nenagh Unions
  www.igp-web.com/tipperary/rateindex.htm

Religious Census
- Ireland 1766 Religious Census
  http://search.ancestry.co.uk/search/db.aspx?dbid=5990
  Pay per view.

Antrim
- Dissenters in the Parish of Ahoghill, County Antrim, 1766
  www.ancestryireland.com/family-records/dissenters-in-the-
  parish-of-ahoghill-county-antrim-176
  Subscription required.

Cork
- 1766 Census Records Diocese of Cloyne, County Cork
  www.ginnisw.com/1766.htm
  Returns of Protestant and Papist families for various parishes.

Donegal
- Names Of Protestant Householders In The Parish Of Leck, Co Donegal,
  1766
  http://freepages.genealogy.rootsweb.ancestry.com/~donegal/
  leck1766.htm

Galway *See also* Roscommon
- Leitrim-Roscommon Elphin Census Database (Synge Census, 1749)
  www.leitrim-roscommon.com/elphin/index.shtml
  Ecclesiastical census, covering parts of Galway, Roscommon, & Sligo.

Louth
- Protestant Parishioners Diocese, Co. Louth, 1802
  www.from-ireland.net/protestant-parishioners-louth-1802
  Diocesan census, 1802.

Meath
- Meath Ireland Church & Parish Records
  www.rootsweb.ancestry.com/~irlmea2/Church/
  Primarily transcripts of the c.1802 Diocesan census for many parishes.
- Protestant Parishioners: Diocese of Meath 1802
  www.from-ireland.net/protestant-parishioners-meath-1802
  Diocesan census, 1802.

Offaly
- Religious Census, Ballycommon, Co. Offaly, 1766
  www.from-ireland.net/religious-census-ballycommon-offaly

Roscommon *See also* Galway
- Find your ancestors in The Census Of Elphin 1749
  www.findmypast.ie/articles/world-records/full-list-of-the-irish-family-history-records/
  Pay per view. The Diocese covers most of Co. Roscommon, plus some parishes in Co's Galway & Sligo.
- Elphin Diocesan Census 1749
  www.irishancestors.ie/?page_id=1688
- Roscommon, St. Peters Parish, 1749 Religious Census
  www.ajmorris.com/dig/toc/rosres.htm
  Scroll down to title. Subscription required.

Sligo *See* Galway & Roscommon

Tipperary
- Religious Census 1766
  www.igp-web.com/tipperary/census1766/index.htm
  For Co. Tipperary.

- County Tipperary Records
  www.irelandgenweb.com/irltip/records.htm
  Scroll down for an index to the 1766 religious census.

Tyrone
- County Tyrone: Census Records
  www.cotyroneireland.com/menus/census.html
  Includes the religious census of 1766 for Aghalow, Artrea, Carnteel, Derryloran, Drumglass, Dungannon, Kildress, & Tulliniskan; also a separate census for Desertcreat, 1834.

Roman Catholic Records
- Irish Roman Catholic records
  www.irishtimes.com/ancestor/browse/records/church/catholic/
- Irish Jesuit Archives
  www.jesuitarchives.ie

School Records and Registers *see also* Teachers, p.126-7.
- Guide to Sources on National Education
  www.nationalarchives.ie/research/research-guides-and-articles/guide-to-sources-on-national-education
  From the National Archives of Ireland; includes details of sources for both teachers & pupils.
- Ireland Schools
  https://familysearch.org/learn/wiki/en/Ireland_Schools
- Local History: 5: National Education Records
  www.proni.gov.uk/no.5_-__national_education_records__55kb_.pdf
  From the Public Record Office of Northern Ireland.
- Introduction: Ministry / Department of Education Archive
  www.proni.gov.uk/introduction__education_archive-2.pdf
  From the Public Record Office of Northern Ireland.
- Primary Education Records
  www.irishfamilyresearch.co.uk/EssentialResource6.htm
  Introduction.

Antrim

- Students at Queen's College, Belfast, 1849-59
  www.ancestryireland.com/family-records/students-at-queens-college-belfast-1849-59
  Subscription required. For non-matriculated students, see
  /non-matriculated-students-at-queens-college-belfast-1849-1859/
- Gracehill Academy: Pupils and Teachers, 1805-55
  www.ancestryireland.com/family-records/gracehill-academy-pupils-and-teachers-1805-55
  Subscription required.

Armagh

- Lurgan School Registers
  www.lurganancestry.com/schoolreg.htm
  Extracts from various registers, 18-20th c.

Carlow

- Index to Carlow Schools
  www.rootsweb.ancestry.com/~irlcar2/schools.htm
  Miscellaneous pages, including some names of pupils & teachers.

Cavan

- Munlough School Register of Pupils from 1866 to 1977
  www.bawnboy.com/local-genealogy/munlough-school-index.html

Clare

- Online Records
  www.clarelibrary.ie/eolas/coclare/genealogy/genealog.htm
  Includes many pages on school registers & roll books.
- History of Education in Clare
  www.clarelibrary.ie/eolas/coclare/history/education.htm
  Includes pages on individual schools.

Cork

- Students at Queen's College, Cork, 1849-59
  www.ancestryireland.com/family-records/students-at-queen%C2%92s-college-cork-1849-59
  Subscription required. For non-matriculated students, see
  /non-matriculated-students-at-queen%C2%92s-college-cork-1849-59.

Donegal

- County Donegal School Records
  http://freepages.genealogy.rootsweb.ancestry.com/~donegal/school.htm
  Includes pages for:
  Derryloaghan National School Register, Inishkeel [Boys 1874-1898.]
  Register of Killybegs Commons School 1867-73.
  Naran National School Register, Inishkeel, 1880-1900.
  Inishkeeragh Island National School [Index to boys' register, early 20th c.]
  Innismeane Island National School Rollbook 1886-1917.
  Newtowncunningham National School No 2, Allsaints [Register of boys', 1902-12, & of girls, 1911-12; also District Inspector's Observation Book, various dates].
  Boy's Register Dungloe National School, Templecrone, Co Donegal: 1873-81.
  Drumbeg National School, Taughboyne; Boys 1902 - 1926 & Girls 1904-28.

- Raphoe Royal School: students names
  http://freepages.genealogy.rootsweb.ancestry.com/~donegaleire/Rapschool.htm
  In 1849.

Down

- School Information from all parishes in Co. Down, Ireland
  http://freepages.genealogy.rootsweb.ancestry.com/~rosdavies/WORDS/Schools.htm
  Database
- Lawrencetown National School
  www.lawrencetown.com
  Includes boys' register, 1870-98, & girls 1880-1923.
- School Records
  www.bagenalscastle.com/ancestry/06_school/01_school.htm
  Includes list of registers for Newry.

Fermanagh

- Educational Institutions
  www.igp-web.com/Fermanagh/Donated.htm#7
  Various lists of teachers and students from Fermanagh, in Excel format.

Galway

Students at Queen's College, Galway, 1849-60
www.ancestryireland.com/family-records/students-at-queen%C2%92s-college-galway-1849-60
Subscription required. For non-matriculated students, see
/non-matriculated-students-at-queen%C2%92s-college-galway-1849-60

Laois

Children Attending Moutmellick Quaker School 1786-1794
www.from-ireland.net/children-attending-mountmellick-quaker-school-laois

Londonderry

- Lislea records
  www.torrens.org.uk/Genealogy/BannValley/church/Lislea
  Includes boys' school enrolment registers 1864-1916, & girls' school enrolment register 1907-13.
- Eden School Register from 1872 to 1945
  www.ancestryireland.com/family-records/eden-school-register-1872-1945/
  School at Tamlaght O'Crilly

Meath

- Ashbourne National School Register of Names from 1870 to 1906
  www.angelfire.com/ak2/ashbourne/reginfs1.html

Tyrone

- County Tyrone: Schools
  www.cotyroneireland.com/menus/schools.html
  Includes registers of various schools.
- Bready Ancestry: School Records
  www.breadyancestry.com/index.php?id=schoolrecords
  School registers for Ballyneaner, 1863-early 1900s, Bready, 1861-1951, Glenagoorland, 1872-1950, & Sandville, 1863-1913,

Solicitors Records

- Local History, 6: Solicitors Archives
  www.proni.gov.uk/no.6_-_solicitors___archives__49kb_.pdf
  In the Public Record Office of Northern Ireland.

- Introduction: O'Rorke, McDonald & Tweed Archive
  www.proni.gov.uk/introduction__o_rorke__mcdonald___tweed_d1242.pdf
  Solicitors archives from Co. Antrim.
- Introduction: Martin & Brett Archive
  www.proni.gov.uk/introduction__martin___brett.pdf
  Solicitor's archive from Co. Monaghan.

State Papers

- State papers Ireland 1509-1782
  www.nationalarchives.gov.uk/records/research-guides/state-papers-ireland-1509-1782.htm
  Advice page.
- Calendar of the State Papers Relating To Ireland, 1633-1647
  www.worldvitalrecords.com/indexinfo.aspx?ix=ia_calendarofstatep02grea
  Pay per view. From printed books.

Taxes *See also* Hearth Tax & Poll Tax
- Ireland Taxation
  https://familysearch.org/learn/wiki/en/Ireland_Taxation

Tithes *See also* Griffith's Valuation

Advice Pages
- Genealogy records: Tithe Applotment Books and the Primary (Griffith's) Valuation
  www.nationalarchives.ie/genealogy1/genealogy-records/tithe-applotment-books-and-the-primary-griffith-valuation
- Your Family Tree: 23. Tithe Records
  www.proni.gov.uk/no.23_-_tithe_records__76kb_.pdf
  Advice from the Public Record Office of Northern Ireland.
- Tithe Records of Ireland
  www.ancestry.com/cs/Satellite?childpagename=USLearning Center%2FLearning_C%2FPageDefault&pagename= LearningWrapper&cid=1265125734248
- Research Help: Tithe Applotment Books
  www.from-ireland.net/research-help-tithe-applotment-books

- Tithe Applotment Books: The earliest records of the poor in Ireland
  www.irish-genealogy-toolkit.com/tithe-applotment-books.html
- Tithe Composition and Applotment Books
  http://freepages.genealogy.rootsweb.ancestry.com/~irishancestors/Tithe%20books.html
- Research Help: Tithe Applotment Books
  www.from-ireland.net/research-help-tithe-applotment-books
- Tithe Applotment Books
  www.irishtimes.com/ancestor/browse/records/land/tiap.htm#Property
- Ireland: a listing of Land Tax or Tithe Defaulters for 1831
  http://home.alphalink.com.au/~datatree/datree1.htm htm
  www.ancestordetective.com/ireland/tithe.htm

National Databases
- The Tithe Applotment Books
  http://titheapplotmentbooks.nationalarchives.ie/search/tab/home.jsp
  Digitised images from the National Archives of Ireland.
- Ireland, Tithe Applotment Books, 1814-1855
  https://familysearch.org/search/collection/1804886
  Over 66,000 images.
- Ireland, Tithe Applotment Books, 1823-1837
  http://search.ancestry.co.uk/search/db.aspx?dbid=1270
  Pay per view.
- Ireland, Tithe War, 1830-1831
  www.worldvitalrecords.com/indexinfo.aspx?ix=eneclann_enec007
  Lists over 29,000 defaulting tithe-payers.

Armagh
- Tithe Applotments
  www.igp-web.com/armagh/records.htm#tithes
  Indexes for many Armagh parishes.

Carlow
- County Carlow Tithe Defaulters for 1831
  www.rootsweb.ancestry.com/~irlcar2/Tithe_Defaulters.htm

Clare
- 1820s-1840s Clare Tithe Applotment Books: Surname Index
  www.clarelibrary.ie/eolas/coclare/genealogy/tithe_applot/name_index/surname_index.htm
- Kilmaley Parish, County Clare Residents 1826 and 1855
  www.ajmorris.com/dig/toc/_01clkm.htm
  Pay per view. From the tithe applotment books and Griffiths' Valuation.

Cork
- County Cork Tithes by Diocese
  http://freepages.genealogy.rootsweb.ancestry.com/~mturner/cork/a_tithes.htm
  Many pages of transcripts of tithe applotment books for particular places
- Tithe Listing for Diocese of Cloyne
  www.igp-web.com/cork/Tithe49.htm
  Covers Co. Cork.
- Tithe Defaulter Schedules for Cork 1831
  www.failteromhat.com/tithe1831.php

Donegal
- Tithe Applotment Books for the Parishes of Killybegs, Upper and Lower, signed 1834
  http://freepages.genealogy.rootsweb.ancestry.com/~donegal/killytithe.htm
- Tithe Applotment Book for the Parish of Templecrone, signed 22 Oct. 1828
  http://freepages.genealogy.rootsweb.ancestry.com/~donegal/templetithes.htm

Fermanagh
- 1823-1838 Index: Tithe Applotment, Fermanagh
  http://timothylunney.wordpress.com/2010/01/23/1823-1838-tithe-applotment-index-fermanagh
  See also
  www.rootsweb.ancestry.com/~nirfer/1825-1835_tithe_applotment_index.htm

Kerry
- Tithe Applotment Survey 1823-37: County Kerry
  www.rootsweb.ancestry.com/~irlker/tithe.html
  In progress; only a few parishes at present.

Heads of Household of Ballyferriter Catholic Parish, Barony of Corkaguiny, County Kerry, Ireland, 1827-1852
www.reocities.com/Athens/Ithaca/7974/Ballyferriter/compilation.html
From tithe applotment books 1827-31, a religious census 1834, and Griffiths Valuation 1851-2.
Tithe Valuation, Brosna Parish, Co. Kerry, Ireland, c.1820
www.bluegumtrees.com/brosnakerry/Griffiths.html

Laois

Tithe Applotment Books, Co. Laois
www.from-ireland.net/tithe-apployment-book-laois

Leitrim

County Leitrim Records: Tithe Applotments
www.irelandgenweb.com/irllet/records.htm
Scroll down for numerous digitised images and transcriptions

Limerick

[Co. Limerick Tithe Applotments]
www.connorsgenealogy.com/LIM/index.htm#land
Scroll down. Includes applotments for many parishes.
County Limerick Tithe Applotment Defaulters 1831
www.connorsgenealogy.com/LIM/TitheDefaulters.htm

Mayo

• County Mayo Research: Tithe Applotments
www.irelandgenweb.com/irlmay/records.htm#tithes
Includes pages for Bohola, Kilmoremoy, Kilmovee, Kilmore, Shrule, Templemore, & Templemurry.

Monaghan

Monaghan, Donaghmoyne, Tithe Index 1823
www.ajmorris.com/dig/toc/monres.htm
Scroll down to title. Subscription required.

Sligo

• Tithe Applotment Books 1823-1834
www.sligoroots.com/sources/other-civil-sources/tithe-applotment-books-1823-1834
Details of an offline database.

• Sligo County Ireland Tithe 1824
www.rootsweb.ancestry.com/~irlsli/tithemcgeeopen.html

Tipperary

• Tithes
www.irelandgenweb.com/irltip/records.htm
Names of occupiers for many Tipperary parishes, from tithe applotment books, 1815-38.
• [Tithe Applotment Records, Tipperary, 1828]
http://freepages.genealogy.rootsweb.ancestry.com/~irish/Tipperary/Tithe1828.htm
• Assorted Tithe Applotment & Tithe Defaulters Records, County of Tipperary
www.igp-web.com/tipperary/tithes/index.htm

• County Tipperary Ireland
www.connorsgenealogy.com/tipp
Scroll down for local tithe applotments 1823-38.
• The Parish of Outeragh, County Tipperary, Ireland
www.ancestordetective.com/ireland/outeragh.htm
Based on tithe applotment book, Griffith's valuation, etc.

Tyrone

• Tithe Applotment Explanation & Index
www.cotyroneireland.com/tithe/titheindex.html
Includes some transcripts.
• Bready Ancestry: Tithe Valuation
www.breadyancestry.com/index.php?id=valuations
Databases for Donagheady, & Leckpatrick, various 19th c dates.

Wexford

• Wexford Census Substitutes
www.igp-web.com/IGPArchives/ire/wexford/censubs.htm
Includes lists of tithe defaulters in Taghmon, 1831.

Transportation Records: General *See also* Emigration
• Transportation of Irish English
www.uni-due.de/IERC/transportation.htm

Transportation Records: Australia
- Sources in the National Archives for Research into the Transportation of Irish Convicts to Australia (1791-1853): Introduction
  www.nationalarchives.ie/topics/transportation/transp1.html
  www.nationalarchives.ie/topics/transportation/Ireland_Australia_
  transportation.pdf
- Irish Convicts Transported to Australia
  www.rootsweb.ancestry.com/~fianna/oc/oznz/pasconau.html
  Introduction, with links.
- Transportation Records 1791-1853
  http://freepages.genealogy.rootsweb.ancestry.com/~irishancestors/
  AusT.html

Databases
- Ireland-Australia Transportation Records (1791-1853)
  www.nationalarchives.ie/genealogy1/genealogy-records/ireland-
  australia-transportation-records-1791-1853
  Includes transportation database. Also searchable (pay per view) at
  www.ajmorris.com/dig/web/autp.htm.
- Convict Records of Australia
  www.convictrecords.com.au
  Database of transportation registers, 1787-1867, searchable by name, year, or ship. Also searchable at
  www.slq.qld.gov.au/resources/family-history/convicts
- Irish Rebels to Australia 1800-1806
  http://members.pcug.org.au/~ppmay/rebels.htm
  Database.
- Irish Convicts to N.S.W. 1788-1849
  http://members.pcug.org.au/~ppmay/convicts.htm
- Irish Rebels to Australia 1800-1806
  http://members.pcug.org.au/~ppmay/rebels.htm
  Database.

Cork
- Mallow Archaeological & Historical Society: Australian Transportation Records
  www.rootsweb.ancestry.com/~irlmahs/trans.htm

Donegal
- Convicts from Donegal to Australia covering the period 1788 to 1868: National Archives of Ireland:
  http://freepages.genealogy.rootsweb.ancestry.com/~donegal/
  iconoz.htr
  List.

Transportation Records: North America
- Early American Crime: The Need for a New Punishment: Early Uses of Convict Transportation
  www.earlyamericancrime.com/convict-transportation/new-
  punishment/early-convict-transportation

Donegal
- People Involuntarily Transported to America from Donegal 1737 to 1743
  http://freepages.genealogy.rootsweb.ancestry.com/~donegal/
  involtrans.htr

Dublin
- A list of Deported Convicts and Vagabonds 1737-1743
  www.ulsterancestry.com/ua-free_Convicts-and-Vagabonds.html
  Convicts transported to North America from Dublin.

Ulster Covenant
- The Ulster Covenant
  www.proni.gov.uk/index/search_the_archives/ulster_covenant.htm
  Database of c.500,000 signatures to the 1912 Ulster Covenant
- The Ulster Covenant
  www.lurganancestry.com/covenant.htm

University Registers
- Alumni Dublinenses, 1924 Edition
  http://search.findmypast.ie/search-world-Records/alumni-
  dublinenses---1924-editio
  From a printed book. Pay per view. Also available (pay per view) at
  www.familyrelatives.com/search/search_alumni_dublinense.php.
- Alumni Dublinenses: Trinity College, University of Dublin, 1593-1860
  www.ancestryireland.com/family-records/alumni-dublinenses-
  trinity-college-university-of-dublin-1593-1860
  From a printed book. Pay per view.

- Trinity College Dublin: Database of Students, 1593-1826
  www.irishfamilyresearch.co.uk/TCDintro.HTM
- Find your ancestors in Registers of Queen's Colleges Ireland 1849-1858
  www.findmypast.com/articles/world-records/full-list-of-the-irish-family-history-records/education-and-work/registers-of-queens-colleges-ireland-1849-1858
  From a printed book. Pay per view.
- Search Royal Belfast Academical Institute Alumni, 1814-1875
  www.ancestryireland.com/family-records/search-royal-belfast-academical-institute-alumni-1814-1875
  Subscription required.

Vaccination Records

Cavan
- Templeport Infants who were vaccinated in the years 1864-1874
  www.bawnboy.com/local-genealogy/vaccinated-children-1864-77.html

Valuation Records *See also* Griffith's Valuation
- Valuation Office: Archives, Genealogy and Public Office
  www.valoff.ie/en/Archives_Genealogy_Public_Office
  Official site.
- Your Family Tree: 4. Valuation Records
  www.proni.gov.uk/no.4_-_valuation_records__81kb_.pdf
- Valuation Office Records
  www.irishtimes.com/ancestor/browse/records/land/val.htm
- The Primary Valuation of Tenements
  http://freepages.genealogy.rootsweb.ancestry.com/~irishancestors/Primary%20valuation.html
- Griffith's Valuation Books - beyond the Primary list of tenements: Advanced research in the pre-publication and post-publication manuscripts
  www.irish-genealogy-toolkit.com/valuation-books.html
- Valuation Revision Books
  www.proni.gov.uk/index/search_the_archives/val12b.htm
  Database covering Co's Antrim, Armagh, Down, Fermanagh, Londonderry and Tyrone, 1864-1933; indexed by place-name only.

Donegal
- County Donegal General Valuation Revision Lists: LDS Film Details
  http://freepages.genealogy.rootsweb.ancestry.com/~donegal/valist.htm

Louth
- 1837 Drogheda Householders (Street)
  www.jbhall.freeservers.com/1837_drogheda_householders.htm
- 1833-1840 Dundalk Union £10 Valuations
  www.jbhall.freeservers.com/1833-0_dundalk_union_valuations.htm
- County Louth. Dundalk Householders 1837
  www.rootsweb.ancestry.com/~fianna/county/louth/loufree1837.html
  From Valuation Office house book.
- 1837 Dundalk Householders: Valuation £5 & over
  www.jbhall.freeservers.com/1837_dundalk_householders.htm
  See also **/1837_dundalk_valuations.htm.**

Roscommon
- Roscommon Land Records
  www.igp-web.com/IGPArchives/ire/roscommon/land.htm
  Includes General Valuation Canceled Books, Electoral District of Kilteevan, c.1911-1920's

Tipperary
- County Tipperary, Ireland
  www.connorsgenealogy.com/tipp
  Scroll down for house books, c.1846-50.

Wills & Other Probate Records

Introductions
- Genealogy records: Wills and testamentary records
  www.nationalarchives.ie/genealogy1/genealogy-records/wills-testamentary-records
- Frequently Asked Questions: Wills and Probate
  www.proni.gov.uk/no.7_-_wills_and_probate__41kb_.pdf
- Ireland Probate Records
  https://familysearch.org/learn/wiki/en/Ireland_Probate_Records

- Wills
  www.irishtimes.com/ancestor/browse/records/wills/index2.

       htm#Wills

  General introduction.
- Research Help: Wills, Administrations and Deeds
  www.from-ireland.net/research-help-wills-administrations-deeds

Indexes, etc.

- *Index to the Prerogative Wills of Ireland 1536-1810* / A.J.Vicars.
  www.ajmorris.com/dig/toc/_01iwpr.htm

  Pay per view. Originally published 1897. Also available (pay per view) at:

  www.findmypast.ie/articles/world-records/full-list-of-the-irish-
       family-history-records/life-events-birth-marriage-death/sir-arthur-
            vicars-index-to-the-prerogative-wills-of-ireland-1536---1810

  www.worldvitalrecords.com/indexinfo.aspx?ix=ia_

       indextoprerogati00vica

  search.ancestry.co.uk/search/db.aspx?dbid=48491

  www.familyrelatives.com/search/search_prerogative_wills.php

  www.irishfamilyresearch.co.uk/PR.HTM (by subscription
- Prerogative Wills, 1510-1856
  www.ancestryireland.com/family-records/prerogative-wills-co-

       antrim-1536-1856/

  Subscription required. Covers Co's Antrim, Armagh, Down, Fermanagh, Leitrim, Londonderry, Mayo & Tyrone.
- Ireland, Calendar of Wills and Administrations, 1858-1920
  https://familysearch.org/search/collection/1921305
- Irish Will Calendars 1858-1878
  www.ancestryireland.com/family-records/irish-will-calendars-

       1858-1878/

  Subscription required.
- Index to Printed Irish Will Calendars 1878-1900
  www.ancestryireland.com/family-records/index-to-printed-irish-
  will-calendars-1878-1900

  Subscription required. Covers all counties.
- Calendars of Wills and Administrations 1858-1920
  www.willcalendars.nationalarchives.ie/search/cwa/home.jsp
  For 1922-82, see **http://nai.adlibhosting.com/brief.aspx**

- Will Calendars
  www.proni.gov.uk/index/search_the_archives/will_calendars.htm
  For Armagh, Belfast, & Londonderry Probate Registries, 1858-1965.
- Find your ancestors in W.P.W. Phillimore & Gertrude Thrift, *Indexes To Irish Wills 1536-1858,* 5 Vols (1909-1920)
  http://www.findmypast.ie/articles/world-records/full-list-of-the-
       irish-family-history-records/life-events-birth-marriage-death/wpw-
            phillimore-and-gertrude-thrift-indexes-to-irish-wills-1536-1858
  Pay per view. Also available (pay per view) at:
  http://search.ancestry.co.uk/search/db.aspx?dbid=9144
  www.familyrelatives.com/articles/details.php?aid=48
- Irish Wills Index
  http://search.ancestry.co.uk/search/db.aspx?dbid=7287
  Database of published indexes to (mainly) wills which have been destroyed. Pay per view.
- Index of Irish Wills, 1484-1858
  www.worldvitalrecords.com/indexinfo.aspx?ix=eneclann_wills
  Pay per view. Index to surviving wills.
- Index of Abstracts, Extracts, and Duplicate Copies of Original Wills, pre-1858
  www.ancestryireland.com/database.php?filename=db_wills_

       pre_1858

  Subscription required. Index to 13,000 copies held by the Public Record Office of Northern Ireland.
- Eustace, P. Beryl, et al, eds. *Registry of Deeds, Dublin: abstracts of wills, 1708–[1832],* 3 vols. 1954–84.
  www.irishmanuscripts.ie/servlet/Controller?action=digitisation_

       backlist

  Digitised books; click on title.
- Registry of Deeds, Dublin, Abstracts of Wills, Volume 1, 1708-1745
  www.worldvitalrecords.com/indexinfo.aspx?ix=gpc_

       registrydeedsdublinwills1708-1745_vol1.

  Continued at
  /indexinfo.aspx?ix=gpc_registrydeedsdublinwills1746-1785_vol2
  Pay per view.
- A little bit of Ireland: Extracted Probates 1630-1655 from Abstracts of Probate Acts in the Prerogative Court of Canterbury
  www.celticcousins.net/ireland/probateabstractscanterbury.htm

- Irish Will Abstracts
  www.from-ireland.net/irish-will-abstracts
  Submitted abstracts for various counties.

Armagh
- Armagh Wills to 1 August 1838
  www.ancestryireland.com/family-records/armagh-wills-to-
  1-august-1838/
  Suscription required.

Cavan
- Probate
  http://home.wavecable.com/~colin/genuki/CAV/Probate.html
  Advice page for Co. Cavan.

Clare
- National Probate Calendar (England & Wales): Clare Entries 1859-1941
  www.clarelibrary.ie/eolas/coclare/genealogy/don_tran/wills/
  national_probate_calendar.htm

Cork
- Bandon Related Wills and Abstracts
  www.bandon-genealogy.com/wills.htm
  Lists of wills in various places.

Donegal
- Co. Donegal Wills, Derry Diocese, 1612-1857
  www.ancestryireland.com/family-records/co-donegal-wills-derry-
  diocese-1612-1857
  Subscription required.

Down
- Wills in the Exempt Jurisdiction of Newry and Mourne
  www.ajmorris.com/dig/toc/_01iw4b.htm
  Pay per view. Digitised from a printed index. Covers 1727-1858.
- Administration Bonds: Down, pre 1848
  www.ancestryireland.com/family-records/administration-bonds-
  down-pre-1848/
  Subscription required.

- Administration Bonds: Dromore, Newry and Mourne Wills, pre 1858
  www.ancestryireland.com/family-records/administration-bonds-
  dromore-newry-and-mourne-wills-pre-1858
  Subscription required.

Dublin
- Quaker Records Dublin: Abstracts of Wills
  www.failteromhat.com/quaker/quakerindex.php
- Quaker Records, Dublin, Abstracts of Wills
  http://search.ancestry.co.uk/search/db.aspx?dbid=48492
  Pay per view. Also available (pay per view) at
  www.familyrelatives.com/search/search_quakers.php

Londonderry
- Co. Londonderry Wills, Derry Diocese, 1612-1857
  www.ancestryireland.com/family-records/co-londonderry-wills-
  derry-diocese-1612-1857
  Subscription required.

Tyrone
- County Tyrone: Wills
  www.cotyroneireland.com/menus/wills.html
  Includes numerous wills and indexes.
- Co. Tyrone Wills, Derry Diocese, 1612-1858
  www.ancestryireland.com/family-records/co-tyrone-wills-derry-
  diocese-1612-1858
  Subscription required. Index only.

List by Diocese
- Find your ancestors in Ardagh Wills 1690-1857
  www.findmypast.ie/articles/world-records/full-list-of-the-irish-
  family-history-records/life-events-birth-marriage-death/ardagh-
  wills-1690-1857
  Pay per view. Index only, from a printed book.
- Wills in the Diocese of Ardfert and Aghadoe
  www.ajmorris.com/dig/toc/_01iw3e.htm
  Pay per view. Digitised from a printed index. Covers 1690-1800.

- Armagh Wills to 1 August 1838
  www.ancestryireland.com/family-records/armagh-wills-to-1-august-1838
  Subscription required. Index only.
- Wills in the Diocese of Cashel and Emly
  www.ajmorris.com/dig/toc/_01iw3a.htm
  Pay per view. Digitised from a printed index. Covers 1618-1800.
- Wills in the Diocese of Clonfert
  www.ajmorris.com/dig/toc/_01iwcl.htm
  Pay per view. Digitised from a printed index. Covers 1663-1857.
- Find your ancestors in Clonfert Wills and Administrations
  www.findmypast.ie/articles/world-records/full-list-of-the-irish-family-history-records/life-events-birth-marriage-death/clonfert-wills-and-administrations-1663-1857
- Wills in the Diocese of Cloyne, 1621 to 1800
  www.ajmorris.com/dig/toc/_01iw2b.htm
  Pay per view. Digitised from a printed index.
- Indexes to Irish Wills - Volume II: Cork & Ross, Cloyne
  www.corkpastandpresent.ie/genealogy/indextoirishwills-corkrosscloyne/
  Digitised edition of Phillimore, W.P.W. *Indexes to Irish wills, vol.II. Cork & Ross, Cloyne*. Phillimore, 1910. Covers 1548-1800. Also available at
  www.ginnisw.com/Indexes%20to%20Irish%20Wills/Thumb/Thumbs1.htm
  www.ajmorris.com/dig/toc/_01iw2a.htm (pay per view).
- Wills in the Diocese of Dromore
  www.ajmorris.com/dig/toc/_01iw4a.htm
  Pay per view site. Index from a published source. Covers 1678-1858.
- Find your ancestors in Deputy Keeper Of Ireland, *Index To The Act or Grant Books, and To Original Wills, Of The Diocese Of Dublin 1272-1858* (26th, 30th and 31st Reports, 1894, 1899)
  www.findmypast.ie/articles/world-records/full-list-of-the-irish-family-history-records/life-events-birth-marriage-death/deputy-keeper-of-ireland-index-to-the-act-or-grant-books-and-to-original-wills-of-the-diocese-of-dublin-1272-1858-26th-30th-and-31st-reports-1894-1899
  Pay per view.

- Dublin, Ireland, Probate Record and Marriage Licence Index, 1270-1858
  http://search.ancestry.co.uk/search/db.aspx?dbid=2719
  Pay per view. From printed books.
- Dublin Wills and Marriage Licences 1800-1858 via NLA Website
  http://familyhistory.nnub.net/notice/show/1848
- Wills in the Diocese of Ferns
  www.ajmorris.com/dig/toc/_01iw1c.htm
  Pay per view. Digitised from a printed index. Covers 1601-1800.
- Wills in the Diocese of Kildare
  www.ajmorris.com/dig/toc/_01iw1d.htm
  Pay per view. Digitised from a printed index. Covers 1661-1800.
- Killala and Achonry Diocese Wills Only: County Sligo, Ireland
  www.rootsweb.ancestry.com/~irlsli/willssligohome.html
  Index only.
- Wills in the Diocese of Killaloe and Kilfernara
  www.ajmorris.com/dig/toc/_01iw3c.htm
  Pay per view. Digitised from a printed index. Covers 1653-1800.
- Wills in the Diocese of Leighlin
  www.ajmorris.com/dig/toc/_01iw1b.htm
  Pay per view. Digitised from a printed index. Covers 1652-1800.
- Find your ancestors in Leighlin Administrations 1700 – 1857
  www.findmypast.ie/articles/world-records/full-list-of-the-irish-family-history-records/life-events-birth-marriage-death/leighlin-administrations-1700-1857
- Wills in the Diocese of Limerick
  www.ajmorris.com/dig/toc/_01iw3d.htm
  Pay per view. Digitised from a printed index. Covers 1615-1800.
- Calendar of Wills in the Diocese of Limerick, 1615-1800
  www.limerickcity.ie/Library/LocalStudies/CalendarofWillsintheDioceseofLimerick1615-1800
- Wills in the Diocese of Derry
  www.ajmorris.com/dig/toc/_01iw5a.htm
  Pay per view site. Index from a published source. Covers 1612-1858.
- Wills in the Diocese of Ossory
  www.ajmorris.com/dig/toc/_01iw1a.htm
  Pay per view. Digitised from a printed index. Covers 1536-1800.

- Wills in the Diocese of Raphoe
  www.ajmorris.com/dig/toc/_01iw5b.htm
  Pay per view. Digitised from a printed index. Covers 1684-1858.
- Index of Wills, Diocese of Raphoe 1684-1858
  http://freepages.genealogy.rootsweb.ancestry.com/~donegal/
  wills.htm
- Donegal Will Index: Diocese of Raphoe, 1684-1858
  www.ulsterancestry.com/ua-free-DonegalWillIndex.html
- Wills in the Diocese of Waterford and Lismore
  www.ajmorris.com/dig/toc/_01iw3b.htm
  Pay per view. Digitised from a printed index. Covers 1645-1800.

Witness Statements
- Bureau of Military History
  www.bureauofmilitaryhistory.ie/index.html
  Database of witness statements. Also includes press cuttings, 1916.
- Memorabilia from the 1916 Easter Rising, its Prelude and Aftermath:
  The Bureau of Military History and the Witness Statements
  www.theeasterrising.eu/087_BMH/B_MHistory.htm

Clare
- Clare Witness Statements 1913-1921
  www.clarelibrary.ie/eolas/coclare/history/witness_statements_
  1913_1921.htm

Limerick See Tipperary

Tipperary
- Irish Bureau of Military History: Witness Statements
  www.limerickcity.ie/Library/LocalStudies/IrishBureauof
  MilitaryHistory-WitnessStatements
  Covers Tipperary and Limerick only.

10. Occupational Records

The occupations of our ancestors generated an immense amount of documentation, much of which is of value to the family historian. An introduction to these sources is provided by:
- Ireland Occupations
  https://familysearch.org/learn/wiki/en/Ireland_Occupations

Apothecaries
- Apothecaries Licensed to Practise 1791-1829
  www.ancestryireland.com/family-records/apothecaries-licensed-
  to-practise-1791-1829
  Subscription required. See also **/apothecaries-licensed-1791-1829**.
  For apprentices, see **/apothecaries-apprentices-1791-1829.**

Blacksmiths
- Blacksmiths registered in Donegal 1833-1843
  http://freepages.genealogy.rootsweb.ancestry.com/~donegal/
  blacksmiths.htm

Brewery Workers
- Web: Ireland, Guinness Archive Index, 1824-2002
  http://search.ancestry.co.uk/search/db.aspx?dbid=9090
  Pay per view.

Children, Deserted
- Find your ancestors in Deserted Children Dublin
  www.findmypast.com/articles/world-records/full-list-of-the-irish-
  family-history-records/institutions-and-organisations/deserted-
  children-dublin

Clergy
- Fasti Ecclesiae Hibernicae: the Succession of the Prelates And Members of the Cathedral Bodies in Ireland
  www.worldvitalrecords.com/indexinfo.aspx?ix=ia_
  fastiecclesiaehi05cott

  Pay per view.

- Ireland: Priests who signed Act for the further Relief of his Majesty's Subjects: Between 1782-1786
  www.igp-web.com/IGPArchives/ire/countrywide/history/
  priests01.txt

Roman Catholic Clergy
- Presbyterian (Seceders) Synod, 1833: Name Index
  www.from-ireland.net/category/miscellaneous/laois-queens-county-miscellaneous/page/2/
- Presbyterian (Seceders) Synod, 1833: Congregation Index
  www.from-ireland.net/presbyterian-synod-1833-congregation
- Roman Catholic Parishes in Ireland, 1836
  www.from-ireland.net/roman-catholic-parishes-1836
  List of parishes and priests.
- Roman Catholic Parishes, 1836: Parish Priest Index
  www.from-ireland.net/roman-catholic-parish-priest-index-1836
- Irish Catholic Church Directories 1836-37
  http://search.findmypast.ie/search-world-Records/irish-catholic-church-directories-1836-37
  Pay per view. From a printed clergy directory.

Armagh
- Armagh Clergy And Parishes
  www.worldvitalrecords.com/indexinfo.aspx?ix=ia_armaghclergypari00lesl
  Pay per view.

Clare
- A list of the names of the Popish Parish Priests, Anno 1704
  www.clarelibrary.ie/eolas/coclare/history/popish_parish_priests_1704.htm

Donegal
- Clergy of Templecrone, Arranmore, Falcarragh, Killult, Raymunterdoney and Tullaghobegley
  http://freepages.genealogy.rootsweb.ancestry.com/~donegal/clergy.htm

Kerry
- List of Popish Parish Priests in Kerry, 1704
  www.rootsweb.ancestry.com/~irlker/popish.html
  www.igp-web.com/Kerry/popish.html

Tyrone
- County Tyrone: Church Priests, Pastors, Rectors and Elders
  www.cotyroneireland.com/menus/priests.html
  Various lists of clergy, etc.

Coastguards
- Coastguards of Yesteryear
  www.coastguardsofyesteryear.org/news.php
- Officers of the Coast Guard, extracted from a copy of the Navy List for 1851
  http://ulsterancestry.com/ShowFreePage.php?id=210

Convicts & Prisoners *See also* Assizes, Court Records, & Transportation in chapter 9
- Ireland, Prison Registers, 1790-1924
  https://familysearch.org/search/collection/2043780
  Database. Also available (pay per view) at
  http://search.findmypast.ie/search-world-Records/irish-prison-registers-1790-1924
- Irish Prison Registers
  www.irish-genealogy-toolkit.com/irish-prison-registers.html
- Irish Prisoners
  www.worldvitalrecords.com/indexinfo.aspx?ix=everton_irishprisoners
  Pay per view. 33,000 names, 1780-1867.
- Ireland: List of those in prison under the Protection of Person and Property Act 1881
  www.igp-web.com/IGPArchives/ire/countrywide/xmisc/
  prison-1881.txt
  Lists supporters of the Irish Land League.

Antrim

- Carrickfergus Criminal Return 1839
  www.ancestryireland.com/family-records/carrickfergus-criminal-return-1839
  Subscription required.

Carlow

- County Carlow Genealogy: Index to Convicts & Felons
  www.rootsweb.ancestry.com/~irlcar2/convict_list.htm
  Miscellaneous pages giving some names.

Donegal

- Donegal Prisoners & Convicts
  http://freepages.genealogy.rootsweb.ancestry.com/~donegal/convicts.htm
  Includes lists of prisoners transported to America 1737 to 1743, & convicts transported to Australia, 1788 to 1868.

Down

- Down County Museum
  www.downcountymuseum.com/home.aspx
  Includes databases of convicts, including those subjected to transportation to New South Wales.

Mayo

- 1849 Co. Mayo, Ireland, Convictions
  http://freepages.genealogy.rootsweb.ancestry.com/~deesegenes/convict.html
  List of convicts.

Tipperary

- Tipperary: Persons arrested under the Coercion Act – 1881
  www.igp-web.com/IGPArchives/ire/tipperary/xmisc/coercion-1881.txt
- Nenagh Gaol: Removal of Convicts
  www.hotkey.net.au/~jwilliams4/tgaol.htm
  List, 1845.

Wicklow

- Wicklow United Irishmen 1797-1804
  http://members.pcug.org.au/~ppmay/wicklow.htm
  Database of convicts.

Cricketers

- Cricinfo: Players/Ireland
  www.espncricinfo.com/ci/content/player/country.html?country=29
  Brief biographical details of Irish cricketers.

Freemen

Clare

- The History and Topography of the County of Clare by James Frost: Appendix I - Freemen, Ennis
  www.clarelibrary.ie/eolas/coclare/history/frost/appendix1_freemen.htm

Dublin

- Dublin City Library and Archives: Ancient Freemen of Dublin
  http://dublinheritage.ie/freemen
  Database
- Freemen Of Dublin City 1774-1824
  http://search.findmypast.ie/search-world-Records/freemen-of-dublin-city-1774-1824
  Pay per view.

Galway

- Galway City Freemen, 1794
  www.from-ireland.net/galway-city-freemen-1794

Limerick

- Freemen of Limerick, 1746-1836
  www.limerickcity.ie/Library/LocalStudies/FreemenofLimerick1746-1836
  For 1836-1927, see
  www.limerickcity.ie/media/Freemen%20from%201844%20on%20%283%29.pdf

- A New List of 170 Freemen admitted between 1672-1680 in Limerick City
  www.limerickcity.ie/media/Freemen%201672-1680%20%281%29.pdf
- Freemen of Limerick, 1746-1836
  www.celticcousins.net/ireland/freemenoflimerick.htm

Londonderry
- Records of the Freemen of the City
  www.proni.gov.uk/index/search_the_archives/corporationarchive-3/freemen-25.htm
  Londonderry; includes various indexes.

Wexford
- Records of Wexford Freemen found in the Liverpool Record Office
  http://freepages.genealogy.rootsweb.ancestry.com/~hibernia/records/wexfordfreeman.htm

Justices of the Peace
- The History and Topography of the County of Clare by James Frost. Appendix IV - Justices of the Peace, County of Clare
  www.clarelibrary.ie/eolas/coclare/history/frost/appendix4_justices_of_peace.htm

Knights
- Knights Bachelor knighted in Ireland
  www.rootsweb.ancestry.com/~fianna/surname/knights.html

Landowners *See also* Landowners' Census in chapter 9
Cavan
- Principal Landed Proprietors 1802
  http://home.wavecable.com/~colin/genuki/CAV/Proprietors1802.htm

Clare
- The History and Topography of the County of Clare by James Frost. Part II. History of Thomond. Book of Forfeitures and Distributions: Baronies
  www.clarelibrary.ie/eolas/coclare/genealogy/survey_distribution/baronies.htm
  Lists landowners, 1641.

Kilkenny
- Landowners Map of County Kilkenny … c.1640
  www.rootsweb.ancestry.com/~irlkik/landomap.htm

Lawyers
- Keane, Edward, Phair, P.Beryl, & Sadleier, Thomas U., eds. *Kings Inn admission papers, 1607-1867.* Irish Manuscripts Commission, 1982.
  www.irishmanuscripts.ie/digital/Kings%20Inns%20Admission%20Papers%201607-1867
  Digitised book.

Leather Trades
- Kelly's Directory of the Leather Trades 1915
  www.failteromhat.com/kelly1915.php

Medical Practitioners
- Find your ancestors in Ireland Medical Directory 1852
  www.findmypast.com/articles/world-records/full-list-of-the-irish-family-history-records/education-and-work/ireland-medical-directory-1852
  Pay per view.
- Find Your Ancestors in Medical Directory for Ireland 1858
  www.findmypast.com/articles/world-records/full-list-of-the-irish-family-history-records/education-and-work/medical-directory-for-ireland-1858
  Pay per view.
- Irish Medical Directory 1872
  www.familyrelatives.com/search/search_irish_medical_directory1872.php
  Pay per view. For the 1932 edition, see
  /search/search_irish_medical_directory1932.php.

Merchants
Antrim
- Merchants and Traders of Belfast 1865
  www.ancestryireland.com/family-records/merchants-and-traders-of-belfast-1865/
  Subscription required.

- Militia Attestations Index 1860-1915
  blog.findmypast.co.uk/articles/about-militia-attestations-index-
                                                                    1860-1915
  Pay per view.

Militia & Yeomanry

- Militia, Yeomanry Lists, and Muster Rolls
  www.proni.gov.uk/no.12_-_militia__yeomanry___muster_rolls__
                                                          75kb_.pdf
  List of sources for Ulster.

Cavan

- Cavan Militia
  http://home.wavecable.com/~colin/genuki/CAV/Military/Militia.html
  Notes on genealogical sources; includes brief list of Chelsea Pensioners.

Cork

- Ireland's Royal Garrison Artillery: Hayes Militia Attestations for County Cork
  www.failteromhat.com/hayesrga.htm

Louth

- County Louth Military
  www.jbhall.freeservers.com/oldIndex.html
  Various pages listing militia men.

Parliamentarians

- Biographies of Members of the Irish Parliament 1692-1800
  www.ancestryireland.com/family-records/biographies-of-the-
                                        members-of-the-irish-parliament
  Pay per view.
- Parliament Election Results 1692–1802
  www.ancestryireland.com/family-records/parliament-election-
                                                  results-1692-1802

Police

- Royal Irish Constabulary Records
  www.nationalarchives.gov.uk/records/research-guides/royal-
                                        irish-constabulary.htm
- Ireland, The Royal Irish Constabulary 1816-1921
  http://search.ancestry.co.uk/search/db.aspx?dbid=6087
  Pay per view.
- Ordering Irish Constabulary Service Records
  www.genfindit.com/ric.htm
- Police History.com: Welcome to the website of the Garda Síochána Historical Society
  www.policehistory.com/index.html
- Police Service of Northern Ireland: Police Museum
  www.psni.police.uk/index/about-us/police_museum.htm
  Includes page on genealogy; the Museum holds copies of the records of the Royal Irish Constabulary, 1822-1922.

Antrim

- Antrim Military & Constabulary
  www.igp-web.com/IGPArchives/ire/antrim/military.htm
  Lists of police, c.1833-58.

Carlow

- Index to Carlow Royal Irish Constabulary & Civil Defence Force
  www.rootsweb.ancestry.com/~irlcar2/RIC_Index.htm

Cavan

- Cavan Military & Constabulary
  www.igp-web.com/IGPArchives/ire/cavan/military.htm
  Lists of police, c.1840-57.

Clare

- Donated Material: Military, Police & Prison Records: R.I.C. Pensions awarded in Clare, 1922
  www.clarelibrary.ie/eolas/coclare/genealogy/don_tran/mil_rec/
                                        ric_clare_pensions_1922.htm

Cork

- Royal Irish Constabulary: Cork Appointees 1816-1840
  http://freepages.genealogy.rootsweb.ancestry.com/~mturner/
  cork/ric_vol1.htm
  Continued at **/ric_vol2.htm** & **/ric_vol3.htm**

Donegal

- Donegal-born Men in The Royal Irish Constabulary (RIC), 1840-1880
  http://freepages.genealogy.rootsweb.ancestry.com/~donegal/
  RICDonegal.htm

Down

- Down Military & Constabulary Records
  www.igp-web.com/IGPArchives/ire/down/military.htm
  Lists of police, 1840-58.

Dublin

- Dublin Military & ConstabularyRecords
  www.igp-web.com/IGPArchives/ire/dublin/military.htm
  Includes list of police, c.1840-58.

Kerry

- Kerry Military & Constabulary Records
  www.igp-web.com/IGPArchives/ire/kerry/military.htm
  Lists of police, 1840-58.
- Kerry R.I.C. Record Excerpts for 1848-1852
  www.rootsweb.ancestry.com/~irlker/ric.html
  www.igp-web.com/Kerry/ric.html
  Co. Kerry police.

Kilkenny

- Kilkenny Military & Constabulary Records
  www.igp-web.com/IGPArchives/ire/kilkenny/military.htm
  Lists of police, c.1840-58.

Longford

- The Genealogy of County Longford, Ireland: Military & Constabulary
  www.igp-web.com/Longford/military.htm
  Includes pages listing Royal Irish Constabulary officers 1816-55, & pensions awarded in 1919.

Louth

- Louth Military & Constabulary
  www.igp-web.com/IGPArchives/ire/louth/military.htm
  Includes lists of police, c.1833-58.

Meath

- Meath Military & Constabulary Records
  www.igp-web.com/IGPArchives/ire/meath/military.htm
  Includes lists of police, c.1833-58.

Monaghan

- Monaghan Military & Constabulary
  www.igp-web.com/IGPArchives/ire/monaghan/military.htm
  Includes lists of police, c.1840-58.

Offaly

- Offaly (Kings) Military & Constabulary Records
  www.igp-web.com/IGPArchives/ire/offaly/military.htm
  Includes lists of police, c.1840-58.

Roscommon

- Roscommon Military & Constabulary
  www.igp-web.com/IGPArchives/ire/roscommon/military.htm
  Includes lists of police, c.1840-58.

Sligo

- Sligo Military & Constabulary Records
  www.igp-web.com/IGPArchives/ire/sligo/military.htm
  Includes lists of police, c.1833-58.

Tipperary

- Some Royal Irish Constabulary Men from Tipperary Mar 1869-Apr 1870
  www.igp-web.com/IGPArchives/ire/tipperary/military/some-ric.txt

Tyrone

- Tyrone Military & Constabulary Records
  www.igp-web.com/IGPArchives/ire/tyrone/military.htm
  Includes lists of police, c.1840-57.
- County Tyrone: The Royal Irish Constabulary 1816-1921
  www.cotyroneireland.com/muster/RoyalIrishConstabulary.html

Waterford

- Waterford Military & Constabulary
  www.igp-web.com/IGPArchives/ire/waterford/military.htm
  Includes lists of police, c.1840-66.

Westmeath

- Westmeath Military & Constabulary Records
  www.igp-web.com/IGPArchives/ire/westmeath/military.htm
  Includes lists of police, c.1840-58.

Wexford

- Wexford Military & Constabulary Records
  www.igp-web.com/IGPArchives/ire/wexford/military.htm
  Includes lists of police, c.1840-58.

Wicklow

- Wicklow Military Records
  www.igp-web.com/IGPArchives/ire/wicklow/military.htm
  Includes lists of police, c.1840-58

Post Masters

- Post Offices in Ireland, 1876
  www.ancestryireland.com/family-records/post-offices-in-ireland-1876
  Subscription required.

Publicans

Carlow

- Applications for Publicans' Liquor Licences c.1904
  www.rootsweb.ancestry.com/~irlcar2/Publicans_Liquor_Licences.htm
  In Co. Carlow

Cork

- 1832: Liquor Licence Applicants, Co. Cork
  http://freepages.genealogy.rootsweb.ancestry.com/~mturner/cork/excise_1832.htm
- Excise Licenses Obtained 1837, Co. Cork
  http://freepages.genealogy.rootsweb.ancestry.com/~mturner/cork/excise_1837.htm

Wicklow

- A List of County Wicklow, Ireland, Publicans in 1910
  www.ancestorsatrest.com/ireland_genealogy_data/co_wicklow_publicans_in_1910.shtml

Rugby Players

- Irish Rugby Football Players, 1880
  www.ancestryireland.com/family-records/irish-rugby-football-players-1880

  Subscription required.

Seamen

- Crew List Index Project
  www.crewlist.org.uk/findingoncrewlists.html
  Includes useful guidance.
- Irish Mariners: Irish Merchant Seamen, 1918-1921
  www.irishmariners.ie/index.php
  Database with 24,000 names.

Clare

- Board of Trade Registrar General of Shipping and Seamen: Central Register of Seamen
  www.clarelibrary.ie/eolas/coclare/genealogy/don_tran/shipping_seamen/botrg_central_reg.htm

Cork

- Admiralty Passing Certificates, Co. Cork, 1782-92
  www.from-ireland.net/admiralty-passing-certificates-cork

Sheriffs

Clare

- Notes on the Sheriffs of County Clare, 1570-1700
  www.clarelibrary.ie/eolas/coclare/genealogy/sheriffs/index.htm

- The History and Topography of the County of Clare by James Frost. Appendix IV - High Sheriffs of Clare
  www.clarelibrary.ie/eolas/coclare/history/frost/appendix4_high_sheriffs.htm

Louth

- County Louth High Sheriffs 1381-1918
  www.jbhall.freeservers.com/1381-_1918_high_sheriffs.htm

Meath

- High Sheriff of Meath
  http://en.wikipedia.org/wiki/High_Sheriff_of_Meath
  List.

Soldiers

- Óglaigh na hÉireann: Military Archives
  www.militaryarchives.ie/en/home/
  Official Defence Forces Ireland site; includes Military Service Pensions Collection database, relating to veterans of the fight for independence 1916-24.
- Finding and Using Irish Military Records
  www.rootsweb.ancestry.com/~fianna/guide/military.html
- Ireland Military Records
  https://familysearch.org/learn/wiki/en/Ireland_Military_Records
- Irish Cavalry Regiments
  http://freepages.genealogy.rootsweb.ancestry.com/~mturner/cork/regiment.htm
  List of regiments with brief notes.
- Genealogy Quest, Ireland: Roman Catholic Officers 1693
  http://genealogy-quest.com/military-records/1693-roman-catholic-officers
- The Irish Pensioners of William III's Huguenot Regiments, 1702
  www.celticcousins.net/ireland/huguenotpensioners.htm

- Find your ancestors in British Army Pensioners, Royal Hospital Kilmainham, Ireland, 1783-1822
  www.findmypast.com/articles/world-records/full-list-of-the-irish-family-history-records/military-service-and-conflict/kilmainham-pensioners---british-army-service-records-1783-1822
  Pay per view database.
- Military Index, 1832
  www.from-ireland.net/military-index-1832
  Index to papers in the National Archives of Ireland.
- Irish Officers in the United States Army, 1865-1898
  www.rootsweb.ancestry.com/~irlker/officers1865.html
- Irish Volunteers for the Papal Army, 1860
  www.ancestryireland.com/family-records/irish-volunteers-for-the-papal-army-1860/
  Subscription required.
- Find your ancestors in Ireland: National Roll of Honour 1914-1921
  www.findmypast.com/articles/world-records/full-list-of-the-irish-family-history-records/military-service-and-conflict/ireland-national-roll-of-honour-1914-1921
  Pay per view database of those who died, compiled from various sources.
- Find your ancestors in Ireland's Memorial Record: World War 1: 1914-1918
  www.findmypast.com/articles/world-records/full-list-of-the-irish-family-history-records/military-service-and-conflict/irelands-memorial-record-world-war-1
  Pay per view database listing almost 50,000 Irishmen who died, from the printed *Ireland's Memorial Records*. Also available (pay per view) at:
  http://search.ancestry.co.uk/search/db.aspx?dbid=1633
  www.worldvitalrecords.com/indexinfo.aspx?ix=eneclann_enec011
  www.ancestryireland.com/family-records/irelands-memorial-records
- Royal Irish
  www.royal-irish.com
  Includes database of c.15,000 soldiers of the Royal Irish Rifles, pre-1922.

- Our Heroes
  http://ourheroes.southdublinlibraries.ie/about/our-heroes
  Biographies of World War 1 officers in the British Army.
- Soldiers' Wills
  http://soldierswills.nationalarchives.ie/search/sw/home.jsp
  Wills mainly from World War I, but some earlier.
- Find your ancestors in WW1 Irish Soldiers Wills
  www.findmypast.ie/articles/world-records/full-list-of-the-irish-family-history-records/life-events-birth-marriage-death/ww1-irish-soldiers-wills-1914-1920
- Guide to the Manuscript Sources for the Study of the First World War in the Public Record Office of Northern Ireland
  www.proni.gov.uk/fww_guide_version_3_july_2014.pdf
- The Irish in Korea: Irish men and women who gave their lives inthe Korean War
  www.illyria.com/irishkor.html

- Irish County Regiments
  www.reocities.com/littlegreenmen.geo/ICR.htm
  List of regiments, post-1882.
- Summary Information Document detailing the Irish Regiments of the British Army up to 31st July 1922
  www.military.ie/fileadmin/user_upload/images/Info_Centre/Docs2/archives_docs/summary_information_document_on_the_irish_regiments_of_the_british_army.pdf

Antrim
- Deserters in Gaol, 1830-1839
  www.rootsweb.ancestry.com/~fianna/county/antrim/ant-misc.html#deserters
  In Antrim.

Carlow
- Index to Carlow Military
  www.rootsweb.ancestry.com/~irlcar2/military_index.htm
  Various lists of soldiers from Co. Carlow.

Cavan
- Genuki: Cavan Militia
  www.sierratel.com/colinf/genuki/CAV/Military/Militia.html

Clare
- Donated Material: Military, Police & Prison Records
  www.clarelibrary.ie/eolas/coclare/genealogy/don_tran/mil_rec/index_mil_rec.htm
  Includes miscellaneous sources for Clare soldiers, eg Chelsea Hospital records, discharge documents, lists of those who served in various corps, etc.

- Kilrush Men engaged in World War I
  www.clarelibrary.ie/eolas/coclare/history/krmen_ww1/krmen_ww1.htm
- North Clare Soldiers in World War I
  www.clarelibrary.ie/eolas/coclare/history/soldiers/north_clare_soldiers.htm
- Ennis Volunteers' Minute Book, 1778
  www.clarelibrary.ie/eolas/coclare/genealogy/ennis_volunteers_minutes1778.htm

Cork
- County Cork Military and Police
  http://freepages.genealogy.rootsweb.ancestry.com/~mturner/cork/a_military.htm
  Links page.
- [Cork Battalion 1916]
  http://freepages.genealogy.rootsweb.ancestry.com/~bwickham/corkbatt.htm

Donegal
- Royal Hospital Chelsea Discharge Document of Army Pensioners: Donegal-born Servicemen
  http://freepages.genealogy.rootsweb.ancestry.com/~donegal/armypen.htm

Down
- The Soldiers of County Down who Served in World War I
  www.rootsweb.ancestry.com/~nirdow/ww1.htm

Kerry
- WWI Officers from Co. Kerry
  www.rootsweb.ancestry.com/~irlker/ww1officer.html
  www.igp-web.com/Kerry/ww1officer.html

Kildare
- Casualty List: Soldiers from Kildare killed or injured during W.W.I.
  www.esatclear.ie/~curragh/casualty.htm
- World War I: Co. Kildare and The First World War
  www.kildare.ie/Library/KildareCollectionsandResearchServices/
  World-War-One/index.asp
  Includes roll of honour.

Limerick
- Limerick and WW1
  http://limerickww1.wordpress.com
  Includes details of soldiers enlisted from Co. Limerick.

Longford
- The Genealogy of County Longford, Ireland: Military & Constabulary
  www.igp-web.com/Longford/military.htm
  Includes militia muster lists for 1799, 1804, 1814, 1824 & 1832.
- Longford at War
  www.longfordatwar.ie
  Database of World War I soldiers.

Louth
- The Returned Army: County Louth Servicemen in the Great War 1914 - 1918
  www.jbhall.freeservers.com/the_returned_army_-_introduction.htm

Munster
- Munster Volunteer Registry 1782
  www.from-ireland.net/limerick-munster-volunteer-registry-1782
  Lists volunteers. See also
  www.rootsweb.ancestry.com/~irlker/munvolunteer.html

Sligo
- The Sligo Regiment of Militia, or 22nd
  www.igp-web.com/Sligo/Military/Sligo_Militia_1793.htm
  See also /Sligo_Militia_1803.htm
- [Pensions Records of Sligo Soldiers]
  www.igp-web.com/Sligo/Military/1796_Military_Pension_
  Records.htm

Wexford
- World War I Wexford Casualties
  http://freepages.genealogy.rootsweb.ancestry.com/~nyirish/
  Wexford%20Casualties%20WW1.html

Spirit Grocers
- Spirit Grocers in Ireland 1838-1844
  www.ancestryireland.com/family-records/spirit-grocers-in-
  ireland-1838-1844
  Membership required

Sportsmen
- Alphabetical Index to Sports Records
  www.proni.gov.uk/index_to_sports_records-2.pdf
  In the Public Record Office of Northern Ireland.
- Séamus Ó Ceallaigh's Great Limerick Sportsmen
  www.limerickcity.ie/Library/LocalStudies/SeamusOCeallaighs
  GreatLimerickSportsmen

Surgeons
- Brief Summary of the Resources at the Royal College of Surgeons Archives
  www.rootsweb.ancestry.com/~irldubli/RoyalCollege.htm

Teachers
- Teachers & Schools, 1826-1827
  www.ancestryireland.com/family-records/irish-teachers-and-
  schools-1826-1827
  Subscription required. Indexes schools & teachers, from a Parliamentary paper.

- 1824 Survey of Irish Schools
  www.rootsweb.ancestry.com/~irlker/schoolsur.html
  General discussion of a source for teachers.

Clare
- Irish Education Enquiry, 1824
  **www.clarelibrary.ie/eolas/coclare/history/teachers/irish_edu_
  enq1824.htm**
  Includes names of teachers in Co Clare.

Limerick
- Schools and School Teachers: Murroe and Boher, Co. Limerick, 1852-1964
  www.geocities.ws/irishancestralpages/murbohlim.html

Tipperary
- Some Tipperary Teachers, 1741-1764
  www.igp-web.com/IGPArchives/ire/tipperary/xmisc/teachers.txt
- County Tipperary
  **http://www.irelandgenweb.com/irltip/Records/Teachers1826
  BaronyOwneyArra.htm**
  List of teachers from the Barony of Owney & Arra, 1826. For the Barony of Upper Ormond, see
  /Teachers1826BaronyUpperOrmond.htm;
  for Lower Ormond see
  /Teachers1826BaronyLowerOrmond.htm.

Wexford
- Extracted from Education Records held at the National Archive, Dublin, Ireland
  **http://freepages.genealogy.rootsweb.ancestry.com/~nyirish/
  WEXFORD%20Teachers%201845-47.html**
  List of teachers in Co. Wexford, 1847.
- List of teachers Barony of Ballagheen, 1824
  **www.igp-web.com/IGPArchives/ire/wexford/xmisc/
  teach-ballagheen.txt**
  There are similar lists for the baronies of Bantry, **/teach-bantry.txt,**
  Forth, **/teach-forth.txt,** Gorey, **/gorey.txt,** Scarewalsh
  /teach- scarewalsh.txt, & Shelburne **/teach-shelburne.txt.**

Tenants, Evicted
- The Irish Ejectment Books
  www.hotkey.net.au/~jwilliams4/eject.htm
  Brief introduction to court records relating to the ejectment of tenants.
- Find your ancestors in Estate Commissioners Offices, Applications From Evicted Tenants, 1907
  **www.findmypast.com/articles/world-records/full-list-of-the-
  irish-family-history-records/census-land-and-substitutes/estate-
  commissioners-offices-applications-from-evicted-tenants-1907**

Clare
- Ejectment Books of County Clare 1816-1835
  **www.clarelibrary.ie/eolas/coclare/genealogy/don_tran/court_rpts/
  ejectments_1816_1835/ejectments1816_1835.htm**
- Tenants evicted in East Clare from 1st January, 1878 to 1st January, 1903
  **www.clarelibrary.ie/eolas/coclare/genealogy/east_clare_
  evictions_index.htm**

Donegal
- Civil Bill Ejectments for the years 1827 to 1833, from the House of Commons Sessional Papers for Donegal
  **http://freepages.genealogy.rootsweb.ancestry.com/~donegal/
  civilbilljctments.htm**

Town Commissioners
- Database of Town Commissioners in Ireland 1828-43
  **www.ancestryireland.com/family-records/database-of-town-
  commissioners-in-ireland-1828-43**
  Subscription required.

Tradesmen

Carlow
- Index to Carlow Traders
  www.rootsweb.ancestry.com/~irlcar2/traders.htm
  Various pages on Carlow tradesmen.

Limerick
- The Guilds of Limerick, 1840
  www.limerickcity.ie/Library/LocalStudies/TheGuildsofLimerick1840
  Lists guild members, ie tradesmen.

11. Miscellaneous Sites

Administrative Areas *See also* Gazetteers

Many county pages (see chapter 7) have topographical pages giving townlands, parishes, etc; these are not individually listed here. For brief general introductions to administrative areas, see:
- Irish Place Names
  www.irishtimes.com/ancestor/browse/records/land/index2.htm
- Administrative Regions of the British Isles
  www.genuki.org.uk/big/Regions
  Includes pages on the Republic of Ireland, and Northern Ireland
- Administrative Divisions of Ireland
  www.rootsweb.ancestry.com/~fianna/guide/land-div.html
- Land Divisions
  http://www.irelandgenweb.com/irllet/land.htm
- Townlands
  http://en.wikipedia.org/wiki/Townland
  Wikipedia article.
- Local History 1: The Townland
  www.proni.gov.uk/no.1_-_the_townland__54kb_.pdf
  Discussion of an important local administrative area.
- Best Internet Genealogy: Irish Placenames
  http://expertgenealogy.com/free/Placenames.htm
- Placenamesni.org
  www.placenamesni.org
  Origins of placenames.

Adoption
- Ireland Adoption Registry
  http://www.adopteeconnect.com/p/a/5
- Adoption Information and Tracing Services
  **www.tusla.ie/services/alternative-care/adoption-services/
  tracing-service/adoption-information-and-tracing-services**

Anglo-Irish
- Anglo-Irish Families in Kilkenny County (1300)
  www.rootsweb.ancestry.com/~irlkik/kfamily.htm

Biographical Information
- *Chalmers' General Biographical Dictionary*
  http://search.ancestry.co.uk/search/db.aspx?dbid=7077
  Pay per view. From a printed book published 1812-17.
- A Compendium of Irish Biography
  www.booksulster.com/library/biography/index.php
- *Concise Dictionary of Irish Biography* / A.J.Crone
  www.ajmorris.com/dig/toc/_01irbo.htm
  Book originally published 1937. Pay per view.
- Prominent Persons Index
  www.proni.gov.uk/index/search_the_archives/online_indexes/
  prominent_persons_index.htm
  Information on c.5,000 people

Clare
- Carlow & Graiguecullen Son's & Daughter's
  www.rootsweb.ancestry.com/~irlcar2/famlies.htm

Cork
- Pike's Contemporary Biographies
  www.corkpastandpresent.ie/genealogy/pikescontemporary
  biographies
  The biographical portion of *Cork and County Cork in the Twentieth Century*.

Down
- People's Names of Co. Down, Ireland
  http://freepages.genealogy.rootsweb.ancestry.com/~rosdavies/
  SURNAMES/Afrontpage.htm
  Information on 800,000 people.

Kerry
- Kerry Records in the Casey Collection
  www.rootsweb.ancestry.com/~irlker/caseykerry.html

Limerick
- Who's Who of Limerick
  www.limerickcity.ie/Library/LocalStudies/WhosWhoofLimerick

Mayo
- Mayo People
  www.mayolibrary.ie/en/LocalStudies/MayoPeople

Ulster
- The Dictionary of Ulster Biography
  www.ulsterbiography.co.uk

Chapman Codes
- Chapman Codes for Ireland
  www.genuki.org.uk/big/irl/codes.html

Easter Rising
- Ireland: the Easter Rising 1916
  www.nationalarchives.gov.uk/records/research-guides/easter-
  rising.htm

Famine
- Sources in the National Archives for Researching the Great Famine
  www.nationalarchives.ie/topics/famine/famine.html
- Ireland, Famine Relief Commission Papers, 1844-1847
  http://search.ancestry.co.uk/search/db.aspx?dbid=1772
  Pay per view. Over 10,000 names.
- Famine Orphan Girl Database
  www.irishfaminememorial.org/orphans/database

Gazetteers
- Ireland Gazetteers
  https://familysearch.org/learn/wiki/en/Ireland_Gazetteers
  Introduction.
- Placename Database of Ireland
  www.logainm.ie/en

- Ireland Topographical Dictionary
  http://search.ancestry.co.uk/search/db.aspx?dbid=7262
  Pay per view. Digitised version of Lewis's *A topographical dictionary of Ireland*. 1837. Important for places. Also available, pay per view, at **www.worldvitalrecords.com/indexinfo.aspx?ix=qcd59_ireland_vol1.**
- Ireland Gazetteer and Surname Guide
  http://search.ancestry.co.uk/search/db.aspx?dbid=3856
  Pay per view.
- Index of Townlands, 1901
  www.irishancestors.ie/?page_id=5392
- The Ire Atlas Townland Database
  www.thecore.com/seanruad
  Database of townlands, parishes, counties, baronies, etc.
- Geographical Index Northern Ireland
  www.proni.gov.uk/index/local_history/geographical_index.htm
  Locates townlands, parishes, baronies & Poor Law Unions, etc.

Cavan
- The Cavan Genealogist: Cavan Catholic Parishes
  www.iol.ie/~kevins/geneo/cat-map.html

Clare
- Clare Civil Parishes
  www.clarelibrary.ie/eolas/coclare/places/parishes.htm
  Gazetteer of civil parishes. See also
  /history/parliamentary_gazeteer_1845.htm

Cork
- Lewis Topographical Dictionary of Ireland: Towns in County Cork
  www.failteromhat.com/lewis.htm

Donegal
- Townlands of Donegal, listed by Parish
  www.reocities.com/Heartland/Estates/6587/Dontown.html
  List.
- Civil Parishes and Townlands of County Donegal
  http://freepages.genealogy.rootsweb.ancestry.com/~bhilchey/
  DonegalMain.html

Down
- Place Names of Co. Down, Ireland
  http://freepages.genealogy.rootsweb.ancestry.com/~rosdavies/
  PLACENAMES/AfrontPage.htm

Kilkenny
- Administrative Divisions of County Kilkenny
  www.rootsweb.ancestry.com/~irlkik/townland.htm

Kildare
- Index of Townlands of County Kildare
  http://kildare.ie/library/townlands/index.asp
- Lewis's Topographical Dictionary 1837
  http://kildare.ie/library/lewis-topographical-dictionary/index.asp
  For Co.Kildare.

Leitrim
- Leitrim-Roscommon Townland Search Page
  www.leitrim-roscommon.com/TOWNLAND/town.html

Limerick
- Limerick Land Divisions
  www.genuki.org.uk/big/irl/LIM/land/landdivisions.htm
- County Limerick Townlands
  www.countylimerickgenealogy.com/limerick_townlands.php

Mayo
- County Mayo: Towns & Townlands
  www.irelandgenweb.com/irlmay/townlands.htm

Roscommon *See* Leitrim
Gentry & Nobility See also Heraldry, & Knights
- Ireland Nobility
  https://familysearch.org/learn/wiki/en/Ireland_Nobility
- Peerage of Scotland and Ireland
  http://search.ancestry.co.uk/search/db.aspx?dbid=7443
  Pay per view. From Debrett's 1808 edition of the Peerage.

- Irish Landed Gentry
  http://search.ancestry.co.uk/search/db.aspx?dbid=6308
  Suscription required. Pedigrees.
- Peerages in Ireland during the 17th Century
  www.rootsweb.ancestry.com/~fianna/surname/dhpeerages.html
- Burkes Peerage & Gentry's Online Database
  www.irishfamilyresearch.co.uk/essentialresource7.htm
- The county families of the United Kingdom, or, Royal manual of the titled and untitled aristocracy of Great Britain and Ireland
  http://search.ancestry.co.uk/search/db.aspx?dbid=29625
  Pay per view. From a printed book.

Heraldry
- Coats of Arms from Ireland and around the world
  www.heraldry.ws/index.html
- Gaelic Irish Heraldry and Heraldic Practice
  www.leitrim-roscommon.com/heraldry/
- Heraldry in Ireland
  www.heraldica.org/topics/national/ireland.htm
- History of the Genealogical Office
  www.irishtimes.com/ancestor/browse/records/genealogical/
  index2.htm#Genealogical
  Successor to the Ulster King of Arms.
- Heraldry
  www.nli.ie/en/family-history-heraldry.aspx
  Resources of the National Library of Ireland.
- Irish Genealogy & Coats of Arms
  www.ireland-information.com/heraldichall/irishcoatsofarms.htm
- Office of the Chief Herald
  www.nli.ie/en/heraldry-introduction.aspx
- Proto-Heraldry in Early Christian Ireland: the Battle Standards of Gaelic Irich Chieftains
  www.heraldry.ws/info/article01.html

Homicides
- Murders in Ireland 1842-46
  www.ancestryireland.com/family-records/murders-in-ireland-
  1842-1846
  Subscription required. List of persons murdered.

Westmeath
- Homicides from 1848-1870 in County Westmeath
  www.igp-web.com/westmeath/wstmurd.html

Huguenots
- French Huguenot Sources
  http://freepages.genealogy.rootsweb.ancestry.com/~
  irishancestors/Hug.html
  Brief introduction.
- The Huguenot Society of Great Britain and Ireland: Irish Section
  www.huguenotsinireland.com
- Huguenot Surnames
  www.rootsweb.ancestry.com/~fianna/surname/hug1.html
- 1696-1996. St. Paul's Church, Portarlington. The French Church
  http://ireland.iol.ie/~offaly/stpauls.htm

Jews
- The Jews of Ireland Genealogy Page
  http://homepage.tinet.ie/~researchers
- Ireland Jewish Records
  https://familysearch.org/learn/wiki/en/Ireland_Jewish_Records
- Irish Jewish Community: Genealogy
  www.jewishireland.org/irish-jewish-history/genealogy/

Journals and Newsletters
- Irish Journals: an introduction
  www.from-ireland.net/irish-journals-introduction
  Valuable listing.
- Archaeological and Historical Journals
  http://tbreen.home.xs4all.nl/journals.html
  Many of the journals mentioned here have genealogical content
- Irish Chronicles Project
  www.ajmorris.com/dig/toc/_011icp.htm
  Email journal, with many transcripts and indexes of original sources. Pay per view.
- All Ireland Sources Newsletter
  www.sag.org.au/component/content/article/17-help/general6/
  74-aisn.html
  Email newsletter published by the Society of Australian Genealogists.

- Irish Roots Magazine Homepage
  www.irishrootsmagazine.com
- The Irish Genealogist Database
  www.irishancestors.ie/?page_id=3039
  Index to journal.
- The Cavan Genealogist
  http://ireland.iol.ie/~kevins/geneo/index_geneo.html
  Email newsletter

Local History
- Local and Parish Histories of Ireland
  www.irishgenealogy.com/ireland/parish-histories.htm
- Island Ireland Genealogy & Local History
  http://islandireland.com/Pages/history/local.html
  Gateway to Irish local history.

Look-Ups
- Books We Own: Ireland & Northern Ireland
  www.rootsweb.com/~bwo/ireland.html
- Ireland Lookup Service
  www.connorsgenealogy.com/IrelandList/lookups.htm
  Lookups offered in various sources.
- North of Ireland Family History Society: Look-up Scheme for Members
  www.nifhs.org/lookups.htm
  Includes list of parish register and monumental inscriptions transcripts available for look-ups.

Carlow
- County Carlow Lookups
  www.rootsweb.ancestry.com/~irlcar2/lookup.htm

Galway
- Galway County Look-up Page
  www.rootsweb.ancestry.com/~irlgal/volunteer.htm

Kilkenny
- County Kilkenny Ireland Lookup Service
  www.rootsweb.ancestry.com/~irlkik/klookup.htm

Louth
- County Louth, Ireland, Lookup Volunteers
  www.rootsweb.ancestry.com/~irllou/Lookup_Volunteers

Meath
- Look Up Volunteers, County Meath
  www.rootsweb.ancestry.com/~irlmea2/Administrative/lookups.htm

Sligo
- County Sligo, Ireland: Lookups by Volunteers
  www.rootsweb.ancestry.com/~irlsli/lookup.html

Maps
- Ireland Maps
  https://familysearch.org/learn/wiki/en/Ireland_Maps
  Useful discussion.
- Bringing Research to Life: The Role of Historical Mapping in Genealogical Research
  www.irishfamilyresearch.co.uk/essentialresource4.htm
- Local History 8: Ordnance Survey Maps
  www.proni.gov.uk/no.8_-_ordnance_survey_maps__51kb_.pdf
  See also
  /local_history_series_-_08_-_ordnance_survey_maps.pdf
- Ordnance Survey Ireland
  www.osi.ie
- Guide to the records of the Ordnance Survey
  www.nationalarchives.ie/research/research-guides-and-articles/guide-to-the-records-of-the-ordnance-survey
- British Library: Large Scale Ordnance Survey maps of Ireland in the Map Library
  www.bl.uk/reshelp/findhelprestype/maps/ordsurvmapireland/lsosmapsireland.htm
- Tom's Big Chest of Old Irish Maps
  http://homepage.ntlworld.com/tomals/Irish_maps_of_S_Lewis_1839.htm
  Samuel Lewis's county maps, c.1839.

- Atlas and Cyclopedia of Ireland
  www.worldvitalrecords.com/indexinfo.aspx?ix=qcd_33_cyclopedia
  Pay per view. Originally published 1900.
- The Down Survey of Ireland
  http://downsurvey.tcd.ie/down-survey-maps.php
  Digitised maps from a survey of confiscated Irish Catholic estates,
  1654-6.
- Maps
  www.irishtimes.com/ancestor/browse/counties/rcmaps/#maps/
  Includes maps of Roman Catholic & Civil parishes, poor law unions, and
  counties.

Donegal
- Maps and Parish & Townlands Lists
  http://freepages.genealogy.rootsweb.ancestry.com/~donegal/
  maps.htm
  For Donegal.

Leitrim
- The Leitrim-Roscommon Map Collection
  www.leitrim-roscommon.com/LR_maps.html

Limerick
- County Limerick Maps
  www.countylimerickgenealogy.com/limerick_maps.php

Mayo
- Mayo County Library: Map Collections Overview
  www.mayolibrary.ie/en/MayoMaps/CollectionsOverview
  Includes estate maps, some with lists of tenants.

Roscommon See Leitrim

Naturalization
- Ireland Naturalization and Citizenship
  https://familysearch.org/learn/wiki/en/Ireland_Naturalization_
  and_Citizenship

Pedigrees
- Irish Pedigrees
  http://search.ancestry.co.uk/search/db.aspx?dbid=7070
  Continued at **/db.aspx?dbid=49208**. Pay per view. From a printed book
  by John O'Hart. Also available (pay per view) at:
  www.ajmorris.com/dig/toc/_01ip00.htm,
  www.worldvitalrecords.com/indexinfo.aspx?ix=ia_
  irishpedigreesor011915ohar.
- Your Family Tree 15: Pedigrees and Genealogical Papers
  www.proni.gov.uk/no.15_-_pedigrees__72kb_.pdf
- Milesian Genealogies
  www.rootsweb.ancestry.com/~fianna/history/milesian.html

Medieval pedigrees
- Ireland Visitation
  http://search.ancestry.co.uk/search/db.aspx?htx=
  BookList&dbid=6611
  Pay per view. Heraldic visitation pedigrees.

Peerage *See* Gentry & Nobility

Rebellion, 1641-60
- 1641 Depositions Project.
  www.tcd.ie/history/1641
  Includes names of many rebels.
- A List of Wexford People Implicated in the 1641 Rebellion.
  www.igp-web.com/IGPArchives/ire/wexford/xmisc/
  rebellion-1641.txt
- Transplanters' Certificates, 1653-1654
  www.ancestryireland.com/family-records/transplanters-
  certificates-1653-1654/
  Subscription required.
- Forfeiting Proprietors in Ireland under the Cromwellian Settlement, 1657
  www.ancestryireland.com/family-records/forfeiting-propietors-
  ireland-1657/
  Subscription required.
- List of Transplanted Irish, 1655-1659
  www.connorsgenealogy.com/IrelandList/

- Restorees of Charles II, 1660
  www.ancestryireland.com/family-records/restorees-charles-ii-1660/

Rebellion, 1689
- Names of those Attainted by James II, 1689
  **www.ancestryireland.com/family-records/names-of-those-
  attainted-by-james-ii-1689**
- Fighters of Derry in 1689
  www.ancestryireland.com/family-records/fighters-of-derry-in-1689
  Subscription required.

Rebellion, 1798
- Dublin Military & Constabulary Records
  www.igp-web.com/IGPArchives/ire/dublin/military.htm
  Includes list of 'Rebels who surrendered in the city of Dublin from 29th
  June to 9th September 1798'.
- Find your ancestors in 1798 Claimants and Surrenders
  **www.findmypast.com/articles/world-records/full-list-of-the-irish-
  family-history-records/military-service-and-conflict/
  1798-claimants-and-surrenders**
  Pay per view database of those who claimed for losses following the
  1798 rebellion, plus some rebels who surrendered.

Carlow
- Carlow Claimants for Losses in 1798
  www.rootsweb.ancestry.com/~irlcar2/losses_1798_1.htm

Clare
- The United Irishmen of North West Clare, 1798
  **www.clarelibrary.ie/eolas/coclare/genealogy/united_irishmen_
  1798.htm**
  Includes list of insurgents.

Dublin
- Rebels Who Surrendered in the City of Dublin From 29th June To 9th
  September 1798
  **www.worldvitalrecords.com/indexinfo.aspx?ix=ia_
  rebelswhosurrend17dubl**
  Pay per view.

Mayo
- Claims of 1798 Loyalists
  www.reocities.com/Heartland/Park/7461/claim1798.html
  In Burrishoole, Co. Mayo.

Wexford
- Protestants Massacred in the Diocese of Ferns: Rebellion of 1798
  **http://freepages.genealogy.rootsweb.ancestry.com/~nyirish/
  Rebelelion%20of%201798%20WEXFORD.htm**
  For a list of rebels executed, see **/Executed 1798.html**
- A list of some of the protestants massacred in the Diocese of Ferns and
  County of Wexford … 1798
  **www.igp-web.com/IGPArchives/ire/wexford/xmisc/ferns-
  prots-1798.tx**

Scots-Irish
- Scottish Settlers In Ulster
  www.ancestryireland.com/family-records/scottish-settlers-in-ulster
  Subscription required.
- Scotch-Irish Research
  www.genealogy.com/00000384.html
  Presbyterian Scots in Ulster.
- Scotch Irish Pioneers in Ulster and America
  **www.worldvitalrecords.com/indexinfo.aspx?ix=gpc0806300469_
  scotch-irish**
  Pay per view.
- Later Scots-Irish Links, 1575-1725
  search.ancestry.co.uk/search/db.aspx?dbid=49221
  Continued at
  dbid=49222 for 1725-1825, and at dbid=49220 for 1725-1825.

Subscribers
- Subscribers to Crawford's History of Ireland, 1783
  **www.ancestryireland.com/family-records/subscribers-to-
  crawford%C2%92s-history-of-ireland-1783**
  Subscription required.

Subscribers to McKenzie's Poems and Songs on Different Subjects, 1810
www.ancestryireland.com/family-records/subscribers-to-mckenzie%C2%92s-poems-and-songs-on-different-subjects-1810
Subscription required.
Subscribers to Samuel Lewis' Topographical Dictionary
www.ancestryireland.com/family-records/subscribers-to-samuel-lewis-topographical-dictionary
Subscription required. 8,483 names.
Contributors to an Envelope Collection for New Mater Hospital, Belfast, 1900
www.ancestryireland.com/family-records/names-of-contributors-to-an-envelope-collection-for-new-mater-hospital-belfast-1900
Subscription required. See also
/list-of-persons-who-subscribed-to-charity-sermon-at-formal-opening-of-new-mater-hospital-belfast-1900,
and
/subscribers-to-building-fund-for-new-mater-hospital-belfast-1894.

United Irishmen *See* Convicts & Prisoners

Subject Index

Place Index

138

Institution Index